Concepts in Creationism

Concepts in Creationism

edited by
E.H. Andrews
W. Gitt
W.J. Ouweneel

EVANGELICAL PRESS
16/18 High Street, Welwyn, Herts, AL6 9EQ, England.

© Evangelical Press 1986

First published 1986

ISBN 0 85234 228 4

British Library Cataloguing in Publication Data
Concepts in creationism.
   1. Creation   2. Evolution — Religious
aspects — Christianity
I. Andrews, E.H.   II. Gitt, W.
III. Ouweneel, W.J.
231.7'65   BS651

   ISBN 0-85234-228-4

Cover illustration: please see chapter 9, pages 221-223.
Typeset by Computerset, Harmondsworth, Middlesex.
Printed in Great Britain by The Bath Press, Avon.

Contents

The contributors

PROFESSOR EDGAR ANDREWS is Professor of Materials at Queen Mary College (University of London) and was formerly Head of the Department of Materials and Dean of Engineering. He graduated in 1953 in theoretical physics, obtained his Ph.D for research in fracture and was awarded the D.Sc for published work in polymer physics. He was awarded the A.A. Griffith medal in 1977. He has published several Christian books, including *From nothing to nature; God, science and evolution; The promise of the Spirit* and *Christ and the Cosmos*. He is an elder of Welwyn Evangelical Church and President of the Biblical Creation Society in Great Britain.

PROFESSOR EBERHARD BERTSCH received his Dipl.-Ing. from the Technische Hochschule, Darmstadt, and his Dr Rer. Nat. from the Universität des Saarlandes. He is Professor der Informatik at the Fernuniversität, Hagen. His published work includes articles on formal language theory, programming language design and query language implementation. In 1984/85 he served as vice-chairman of the department of mathematics and computer science. He is a member of the Brethren church.

MR DENNIS W. CHEEK holds a B.A. from Towson State University and an M.A. in historical studies from the University of Maryland, Baltimore County. At present he is science department chairman at Bitburg American High School and an auxiliary Protestant chaplain at Büchel AFB, W. Germany. He is the founder and past president of the Baltimore Creation Fellowship and has published an article in the *Creation Research Quarterly* (1981).

DR CHRIS DARNBROUGH received his M.A degree and a Ph.D in biochemistry from the University of Cambridge (1973). He has held research positions in the Universities of Cambridge, Edinburgh and Glasgow, working on molecular biology, most recently as Research Fellow in the Department of Biochemistry, Glasgow University, studying the molecular genetics of the immune response. He is an elder in the church of Scotland at Kenmure Church in Bishopbriggs.

MR GERALD DUFFETT is Head of Biology at the City of Ely College, Cambridgeshire (until July 1986) and formerly occupied similar posts at Luton Grammar/Technical School and Soham Grammar School. He has a B.Sc. degree and a research degree in Zoology from London University. He has written several creationist articles and a technical monograph 'Archaeopteryx lithographica reconsidered'. He is a member of Soham Baptist Church.

PROFESSOR DR-ING. WERNER GITT received his degree as a certified engineer from the Technical University, Hannover, in 1968 and his doctoral degree from the Technical University, Aachen, in 1970. In 1971 he joined the Physikalisch-Technische Bundesanstalt, Braunschweig, as head of the Data Processing Group. Since 1978 he has been Director and Professor. His main areas of scientific work cover systems identification, information theory and numerical mathematics. He is a member of the leader group of 'Wort und Wissen', the only organized creationist society in Germany. He has published many articles and several books on Christian subjects including *Schöpfung oder Evolution; Logos oder Chaos; Denken; glauben; leben; Am Anfang war die Information; Das biblische Zeugnis der Schöpfung; Horizonte überwinden; Das Fundament;* and *Energie -optimal durch Information.*

DRS HENDRIK ROELOF MURRIS has a doctorandus degree in marine ecology and oceanography (Netherlands Institute for Sea Research) and terrestrial animal ecology and plant systematics (the Free University of Amsterdam). At present he teaches biology at the Pieter Nieuwland College in Amsterdam and at the Evangelische Hogeschool in Amersfoort. His scientific studies concern theoretical biology, especially the creation/evolution controversy. He is a member of the Christengemeente te Amstelveen (Congregation of evangelical Christians) in Amstelveen.

DR SIEGFRIED SCHERER is Research Associate in the Department of Biology at the University of Konstanz. He graduated in biology, obtained his Dr Rer. Nat. for research in the physiology and biochemistry of blue-green algae, and was awarded the BYK Research Prize in 1984. His scientific publications include papers on the physiology, biochemistry and bio-energetics of cyanobacteria, the taxonomy of the Anatidae, and on theoretical evolutionary biology. He is a member of the Evangelische Stadtmission Konstanz.

DR WILLEM J. OUWENEEL studied biology at the University of Utrecht and took his doctoral examination *cum laude* in 1967 in genetics and experimental embryology with experimental plant taxonomy as a minor subject. In 1970 he was awarded a doctorate in mathematics and natural science at the University of Utrecht on a thesis entitled 'Genetics, morphology and development of homoeotic wing tissue in the eye of *Drosophila melanogaster'*. From 1971 to 1976 he carried out further research on *Drosophila* at the Royal Dutch Academy of Sciences. In 1976 he was co-founder of the 'Evangelische Hogeschool' (Evangelical College) in Amersfoort where he holds an appointment as part-time professor teaching philosophy and psychology. He is also a part-time minister of the Word and an author.

DR DAVID ROSEVEAR has a doctorate in organo-metallic chemistry from the University of Bristol and is senior lecturer at Portsmouth Polytechnic. He is chairman of the Creation Science Movement and worships at Cosham Baptist Church.

Foreword

Rev. Walter Lang

I am pleased to provide this foreword to the collected proceedings of the first European Creationist Congress. In my own country, the United States of America, the creationist movement has made great strides during the past twenty-five years. It is no coincidence that this period began with the publication of the book *The Genesis Flood* by Henry Morris and John Whitcomb, which demonstrated that the Noahic flood offers an alternative explanation for the formation of the geological column, with its fossil remains, to that provided by evolution. Well written and thoroughly documented, this book has had a tremendous impact, setting forth as it does the religious and scientific value of the creation position.

Since that time, we have seen the formation of several groups in the U.S.A. devoted to the promotion of creationism, including the Creation Research Society in 1964 and the Bible Science Association, of which I have the honour to be Director, in 1963. The creationist movement in Europe is not, of course, a recent phenomenon. In the 1930s a British scientist, Douglas Dewar, who had also spent a considerable time in India, began speaking up for creationism. As a biologist he worked on a scientific basis and also wrote a book entitled *The transformist illusion*. He was one of the founders in England of the Evolution Protest Movement (which later became the Creation Science Movement). Branches of this organization were later formed in Australia (where the vigorous Creation Science Foundation is doing excellent work), British Columbia, South Africa and the U.S.A. A variety of national creationist organizations are now active in Europe and many were represented at the congress.

The theory of evolution is dominant world-wide. Approximately ninety-eight per cent of schools world-wide teach that the universe is billions of years old and that man evolved from lower forms of life. Communists need evolution as a base for their philosophy and they control one half of the world population. While visiting India in March of 1983, I toured the National Museum of India in Calcutta; its displays are dedicated to evolution. I have visited the Mid-East three times and found that schools, whether they be Arab, Moslem, Jewish or whatever, mostly are teaching that the universe is billions of years old and that man is the product of an upward evolution. In Peru, in South America, universities teach evolution without giving any alternative. Even in Africa evolutionary teaching is dominant. In Japan the teaching of evolution is more dominant than Shintoism. This is true also in Korea and Taiwan. We already know that in Europe, Canada and the U.S.A. evolution is the dominant theory taught in schools. It is not just a model of origins; it has become a pagan religion. Many people fear nuclear power; they ought to fear the effects of the teaching of this pagan religion even more. Creationists need not fear, for their God sits in heaven and, according to Psalm 2, he is laughing at these feeble attempts to dethrone him.

When our Saviour neared the time of his suffering and death, he prepared his disciples by telling them what would happen. They did not understand what he was telling them, but later this preparation was of comfort to them. In his high-priestly prayer Christ prayed that none of the twelve would be lost except the son of perdition, the betrayer (John 17:12). None was lost except Judas. One reason was that they had been prepared. So, also, preparation is necessary world-wide for a conflict which will intensify.

One way to prepare is to recognize the value of the spiritual in science disciplines and the value of science in the spiritual. In an era when even ethics are claimed to be flexible, we need courage such as the early Christians had. A flexible morality cannot produce that kind of courage. This means that church people, leaders and members, must be aroused to recognize the value of creation-oriented science.

During the past twenty-five years creationists have concentrated on the science disciplines. There was a need to demonstrate that creationists have produced a superior science, based on a young age for the earth. With the opposition becoming ever more antagonistic, it is extremely difficult to reach scientists and educators. This spells battle, a type of battle not new to the Christian church. But the church will not have the determination unless its members are aroused from apathy. The need at present, and perhaps for the next twenty-five years, is to arouse church members over the creation/evolution issue as they are now disturbed over the issues of abortion and humanism.

In closing we mention three levels of creationism: secular creationism, religious creationism and grace creationism.

The first level, secular creationism, is the level on which we have been working these past twenty-five years to establish the creationist movement. It has been believed that, from a purely natural position, it could be proved that the creation position is a superior explanation for what is observed in nature. We ought to have demonstrated how illogical and unscientific it is to suggest that everything developed through the forces of chance, time and the environment. In this connection the Two-Model approach has been developed in attempts to avoid mention of religion. This approach was good salesmanship and it achieved some success. A creationist foundation has been laid. But there are problems. As Christians we are not interested in a solely secular creationist position. God demands a total dedication.

Thus, the next level is needed. If Scripture and science are to be joined, and if this results in improved research, motivation must come mainly from the churches. Church leaders must also overcome their prejudices against science. By eliminating science from our church life we restrict the power of the gospel to matters which we classify as spiritual. But Jesus Christ was born as a flesh-and-blood being and he died also as a human being. Had he been only a spiritual being, he could not have been our complete Substitute. Because of this second level, our task in the near future is to arouse church people to understand this second level and to grasp its importance.

To understand and appreciate the third level requires a mature Christianity, but the highest levels in science cannot be attained without it. To explain what we mean, think of Elijah living in a cave in discouragement (1 Kings 19:9-13). There was a great wind, an earthquake and a fire; but God was not present in any of these. God was in the still, small voice. The law is not God's greatest power, but his highest power is in his love and his grace. This was represented by the still, small voice. Far more can be achieved through love than through all the armies in the world combined. This applies also to science. The truly great scientists of the past were people who not only accepted the creationist position, but also were motivated by the love of God in Christ. I detect this kind of greatness in scientists such as Maxwell, Faraday, Newton, Kepler and Pasteur.

This means that we need to use the Lord's weapons. It is our contention that if in pre-Civil War days in the U.S.A., slave-owners in the South had been gently persuaded to release their slaves rather than commanded to do so, the Civil War might have been avoided. Though it may take longer, it has happened in other nations. Teachers ought not to be forced to teach the creation position on origins but, on the other hand, Christian children need protection from indoctrination by teachers who teach evolution as a proven fact.

When we understand the grace perspective, we also understand the total gospel preached by St Paul in Colossians 1:18. When he teaches that Christ is to be pre-eminent in all things, he is including science. In Colossians 3:17 Paul says that whatever we do or think ought to be done in the name of Christ. When Christians apply the gospel to material things, they have a better understanding. An illustration of the third level, the grace level, is found in the book of Job. Here we find science in the illustrations from nature. There are many challenges to scientists in the book of Job, but even righteous Job accused God of injustice. He departed from the Lord and his three friends were of no help. They accused Job of committing a special sin for which he was being punished. But the young man Elihu, whom some describe as an upstart, led Job into the gospel. This brought peace to Job and he recognized that his afflictions flowed from mercy, not from judgement. Then followed the whirlwind talk between Job and God in which we find tremendous scientific challenges. Job realized that God is far greater than he could ever imagine. Job received from God's loving hand twice as much as he had possessed before and he will do the same for us. In the book of Job we have before us an illustration of the third level of creationism. It is the total gospel.

Editorial preface

This book contains papers delivered at the first European Creationist Congress, held at Heverlee, Belgium during 22-25 August 1984. The meeting was organized by the Foundation for the Advancement of Studies Faithful to the Bible, Amersfoort, Netherlands and attracted delegates from Australia, Chile, France, Great Britain, Netherlands, Sweden, Switzerland, U.S.A. and West Germany. The purpose of the meeting was to bring together creationists, from a variety of national backgrounds and situations, to discuss a wide range of topical issues. Thus the contributions covered subjects as diverse as the origin of species and the Christology of creation.

In spite of the diversity of subjects, the papers collected in this volume do reveal an interesting measure of coherence at the conceptual level (whence the choice of title for the book). The fundamental concept which unites these chapters is the 'holistic' nature of true knowledge. That is, knowledge is a unity or whole. It may be broken down into many constituent parts for the convenience of study (history, theology, philosophy, science, for example), but at the end of the day all knowledge must be part of a single totality of truth in which the separate components exist in harmonious relationship one to the other. This totality of truth, Christians believe, is to be found in the God and Father of our Lord Jesus Christ, and its outlines stand revealed in Scripture.

There is much confusion over this matter. Members of the scientific community, for example, point out that science has only been free to advance since it was liberated from the shackles of medieval theology. Galileo is the great example. Atheists proceed from this point to conclude that the material or scientific realm is the only reality, while Christians frequently adopt a 'complementary' approach which sees science and Scripture as giving different accounts of being, which are nevertheless equally valid.

Neither of these views is correct. While there is a level at which the different aspects of human knowledge need to be kept discrete, there is a higher level at which they must be synthesized. The error of complementarity is that it places Scripture alongside science. Creationism, and indeed, Christianity, places science, history and the humanities side by side, but sets Scripture above them all as the Word of God in which all branches of human knowledge find their source and significance. The sovereign God is equally the Lord of nature, of history and of all human achievement.

Seen in this light, the combination in one volume of papers on biblical issues, psychology, history, anthropology and biology appears natural and proper, especially as each author seeks to relate his field of study to the higher level at which the terms 'creation' and 'Creator' have significance. The foundations for this higher level synthesis are laid in the opening essay by one of us, but the concepts introduced there are echoed throughout the book.

We hope therefore that this book will not be seen merely as a collection of independent papers with little or no relationship other than the occasion on which they were delivered. The collection epitomizes creationism as a holistic biblical view of being in which the diverse fields of human endeavour can be seen as part of a greater whole. Inevitably, the God-centred nature of that 'whole' must affect the presuppositions of our detailed, lower-level research. Thus the biblically educated scientist sees his 'natural laws' as an expression of the mind of God. The historian views history as the outworking of the plan of God. The student of the humanities sees man as made in the image of God, but also as a fallen creature needing reconciliation to his Creator through the death of Christ.

These chapters, we believe, will serve to illustrate and illuminate these concepts and demonstrate that scholarship may be effective and still 'acknowledge him' from whom all wisdom flows.

Edgar Andrews
Werner Gitt
Willem Ouweneel

PART I

Biblical Concepts

1.

The biblical teaching concerning creation*

Werner Gitt

Introduction

We will tackle our subject, the Bible's teaching on creation, beginning with general points and becoming more specific. We will start with a thorough consideration of the Bible, taking into account its value as information, its truth content and the extent of its subject matter with regard to various domains of reality. Then we turn our attention to the creation narrative as a part of the Bible; and in the last section we pick one example from the creation and use it to illustrate the planning, the wealth of ideas and the wisdom of the Creator.

1. The Bible: a unique source of information

1.1 Distinguishing between various domains of reality
Figure 1 shows various regions which either contain everything (the complete set) or are contained by (subset) or overlap with (intersection) another region. Note that the sizes of the regions in the figure are no indication of their real relative sizes. Consideration of the individual areas in detail should help us to understand the message of the Bible better and to arrange its statements systematically.

(*) Translation from German to English by Christopher and Ruth Gibbs, Berlin.

Region A: This region encompasses the whole of reality and contains our three-dimensional space-time world as a subset. **A** also contains all of God's world, to us at present invisible, of which the Bible says, 'No eye has seen, nor ear heard, nor the heart of man conceived what God has prepared for those who love him' (1 Cor. 2:9).

Region B: This large circle represents our three-dimensional space-time world, including all the perceivable world from the micro- to the macrocosmos, i.e., everything belonging to the earth and also all the still largely unexplored universe. According to Genesis 1, God created this area **B** in six days. Materialistic philosophy on 'the other hand maintains that this material world has always existed in some form and will always exist; thus Friedrich Engels, the co-founder of Communism, said, 'The material, perceptual world, to which we ourselves belong, is the only reality.' When Heinz Zahrnt (German modern theologian) can write, 'For us there is *only one* reality which surrounds us and in which we live,' modern theology has come disturbingly close to the materialist position. Materialism and modern theology also are, accord-

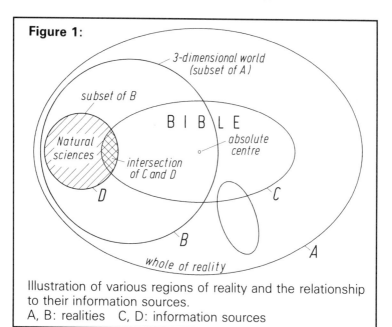

Figure 1:

3-dimensional world (subset of A)

subset of B

B I B L E

Natural sciences

absolute centre

intersection of C and D

D

C

B

A

whole of reality

Illustration of various regions of reality and the relationship to their information sources.
A, B: realities   C, D: information sources

ing to the Bible, on a fatally wrong track. This material, perceptual space-time world is intrinsically finite and impermanent, as Jesus testifies (Matt. 24:35; Rev. 21:1), having been made with an end in view: 'Of old you laid the foundation of the earth, and the heavens are the work of your hands. They will perish, but you endure; they will all wear out like a garment' (Ps. 102:26-27). 'All the host of heaven (= stars) shall rot away, and the skies roll up like a scroll' (Isa. 34:4).

The region indicated by '**A** minus **B**' is the invisible world which is, unlike **B**, eternal: 'For the things that are seen [region **B**] are transient, but the things that are unseen [**A** minus **B**] are eternal' (2 Cor. 4:18).

In Figure 1 an absolute centre of the whole of reality is shown. The New Testament describes this focal point of existence in Colossians 1:16-17: 'For in him all things were created, in heaven and on earth, visible and invisible, whether thrones or dominions or principalities or authorities — all things were created through him and for him. He is before all things, and in him all things hold together.'

This central point of reality is a person: Jesus Christ. As far as **B** is concerned Christ is near the edge: the established sciences take no notice of him, although he is the Designer and Creator of all the subjects of scientific investigation. The laws of planetary motion are his conception just as are the phenomena that physicists investigate in quantum mechanics. The brilliant system of information transfer in cells by DNA molecules and the miracle of bird flight are equally his work. In most people's lives, however, Jesus is the 'stone that the builders rejected' (Ps. 118:22; Matt. 21:42), so that the statements in John 1:10-11 remain the saddest in the Bible: 'He was in the world, and the world was made through him, yet the world knew him not. He came to his own home, and his own people received him not.'

Now that we have looked at the two largest domains of reality, we will consider the sources from which we get our information about them. The two most important sources are the Bible (**C**) and the natural sciences (**D**). In Figure 2 other sciences are given as examples.

The area covered by biblical statements includes both our three-dimensional world and the invisible world. Many an argument about the Bible would vanish if it were made clear in detail which domain was under discussion and what sources of information about it were available. We will now discuss biblical and scientific statements, noticing that one must be aware which region is under consideration.

1.2 The Bible speaks about Jesus Christ

In the Bible, Christ is the central theme; in region **C** Jesus Christ is the central point, as indicated on the diagram. Even the Old Testament is full of prophecies pointing to the Messiah. Jesus could with justification claim that the Old Testament spoke of him: 'You search the scriptures, because you think that in them you have eternal life; and it is they that bear witness to me' (John 5:39).

Paul had also only one central theme, Christ, in his preaching: 'For what we preach is not ourselves, but Jesus Christ as Lord' (2 Cor. 4:5), and all the apostles had this same central concern (Acts 8:32,35; 10:36,42; 11:20; 1 Cor. 1:23; 2 Cor. 1:19; 11:4), and it must be the same now in all our preaching. It is not possible to make Christ known without preaching the Word, and it is hardly possible to make the Word known without preaching Christ.

A scientist recently explained to me some novel ideas of his. I was so fascinated by them that I recommended him to give a lecture on them, but was impressed by his answer: 'I can't do that yet: I must develop the idea fully, and I will only have done that when it leads to Christ.'

1.3 The Bible speaks about faith

The Bible is the central book on faith. We find the definition of faith in Hebrews 11:1: 'Now faith is the assurance of things hoped for, the conviction of things not seen.'

In Figure 2 faith is represented by region 8. Everything pertaining to God's eternal world is available to us only by faith. The Bible informs us about resurrection and judgement, about the return of Christ, about heaven (regions 8,9) and also about hell (region 10). The information is sufficient for our present situation even if it is not complete, so that most of it is not accessible to our sight (region 9). This area, so important for faith and doctrine, has been thrown out, lock, stock and barrel, by 'demythologization' theology, and Bultmann and his followers have led many astray. For Bultmann everything is 'done away with': 'Gone are the

Figure 2:

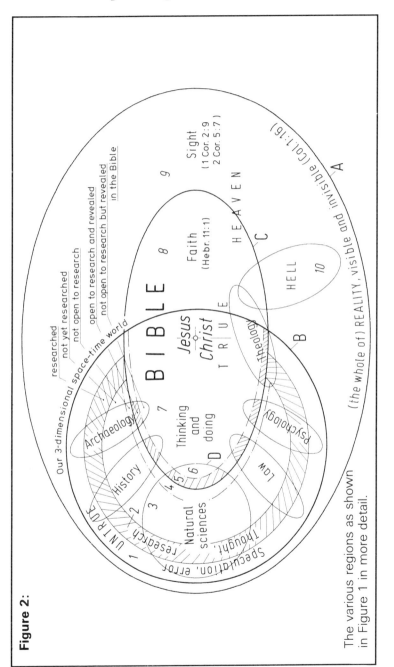

The various regions as shown
in Figure 1 in more detail.

stories of the descent and ascension of Christ, as is the concept of an end of time breaking in, accompanied by cosmic catastrophes; the expectation of the Son of Man coming on the clouds of heaven is no more, and miracles, as mere miracles, are done away with.'

But Christ came to win mankind for heaven, to give us eternal life, to save us, and it was nothing other than the inconceivable cost of salvation on the cross that could procure our eternal home. The author has described the nature of this heaven in the book *Denken, glauben, leben*.[1]

1.4 The Bible speaks of thinking and doing

The Bible is a very varied book, a book concerning
— faith (region 8 in Fig. 2)
— thought (regions 5,6,7)
— living (region 7).

The best laws ever given to man are those found in the Bible: there are no better principles for living to be found in the world than God's commandments. They regulate both human relationships and man's relationship with God. Any engineer building a bridge, aeroplane or turbine must follow exactly the laws of statics, properties of materials or fluid flow, if the construction or machine is to fulfil its purpose without malfunction or breakage. It would never occur to an engineer to invent his own set of laws on which to base the calculations for his construction. In the same way there are unbreakable spiritual laws in ethics which it is essential to obey in order to fulfil God's ordained purpose for human existence. If we abandon these divine commands, immeasurable damage will result. Thus the Bible is no book of mere theory but an unceasing challenge to action, as shown by the following verbs:
— do (Matt. 7:26)
— obey (Exod. 20:1-17; Jer. 7:23; Acts 5:29)
— receive (Acts 2:41)
— know (Ps. 100:3; 1 Cor. 13:12)
— realize (Acts 10:34)
— follow (John 21:22)
— serve (Ps. 100:2; John 12:26)
— forgive (Eph. 4:32)
— store up (Matt. 6:20)
— seek (Matt. 6:33)

1.5 The Bible and science

One of the most fascinating current questions is 'What do science and the Bible have in common?' All controversial issues of our time, such as creation/evolution, theology of revolution, feminism, are dependent on the one basic question: 'How do I read the Bible?' The following questions in particular are of the utmost importance.

What value do we afford biblical statements?

Are biblical statements limited to their time or universally valid?

What are the limits of the Bible's applicability?

Does the Bible really speak with the authority of the living God, or is it a merely human production?

Has the content of the Bible been altered, or do we trust God enough to believe that no influence through all the centuries can obscure or obliterate the information God intended his Word to convey?

There are many different attitudes to the Bible, but many of them can be covered by the following three statements.

1. The Bible is a book concerning only faith and conduct and neither possesses nor claims any authority in scientific matters. Even if there are sporadic references touching on the sciences, they correspond to the contemporary world view or are mixed with the mythical and philosophic imagery of Israel's neighbours at the time, such as the Babylonians, Greeks or Egyptians. Thus modern science is free to continue as it pleases without concerning itself at all with what the Bible says. Knowledge and faith are to be strictly separated. Thus a teacher of religion, Heinz Willner, writes, 'We must ask ourselves whether the obviously antiquated creation texts of the Bible have any place in today's classroom.'[2]

2. The Bible contains here and there useful comments of a scientific nature, but they are not to be taken literally. The Bible offers us no useful, and certainly no definitive scientific material, being as it is a book influenced by its historical circumstances; its only purpose with regard to nature is to testify, as God's Word spoken by men, that it is all God's work.

3. The Bible has the status of a scientific textbook dictated by God.

A thorough consideration of the subject in biblical and scientific perspective shows that all three positions are untenable. Hence we will now define our standpoint with regard to the Bible, derived from its own testimony.

The Bible was not 'handed down from heaven', yet it is a divine book in the sense that the human authors were led by the Holy Spirit. God supervised the writing of the original texts, even including the choice of linguistic expression. Thus the Bible bears the seal of truth and all its statements are binding, irrespective of whether they are about faith, salvation or everyday life, or whether they touch on scientific matters. However, the Bible has at the same time a human element in that the personality of the author was not overridden in any way: each wrote according to his individual manner and literary style. In situations involving a personal commitment the author's moods and emotions come to the fore (experiences with God, meetings with Jesus, times of joy or of sorrow, prayers for help or of thanks or praise) and are completely absent in particular when the author precedes the message with words such as 'thus says the Lord' or 'the word of the Lord came to me'. In the latter case there were many instances of messages which the author understood only partly or not at all. Thus scientific statements inevitably exceeded the current state of knowledge, and prophetic messages usually went beyond the extent of historical understanding (e.g. Dan. 12:8).

Having stated our position, we want to take the Word of God seriously in all its contexts. If we twist the Scriptures we miss God's message to us and cut off access to an irreplaceable source of information. Figure 2 shows how scientific and biblical statements can overlap or have no common point. Figure 3 is an extract demonstrating generally the relationship between scientific and biblical matter, differentiating between areas of science open to research and those not open. Both areas can themselves be included or not in biblical revelation. The resulting four squares have a number of sources of information $Q = 0$ to 2: none, only science, only the Bible and the Bible and science.

Numbers are drawn in Figure 3 corresponding to those in Figure 2. We will now consider the individual regions 1 to 6 as shown in Figure 2. The sciences given are only examples; in

Figure 3:
Relationships between the Bible and science.

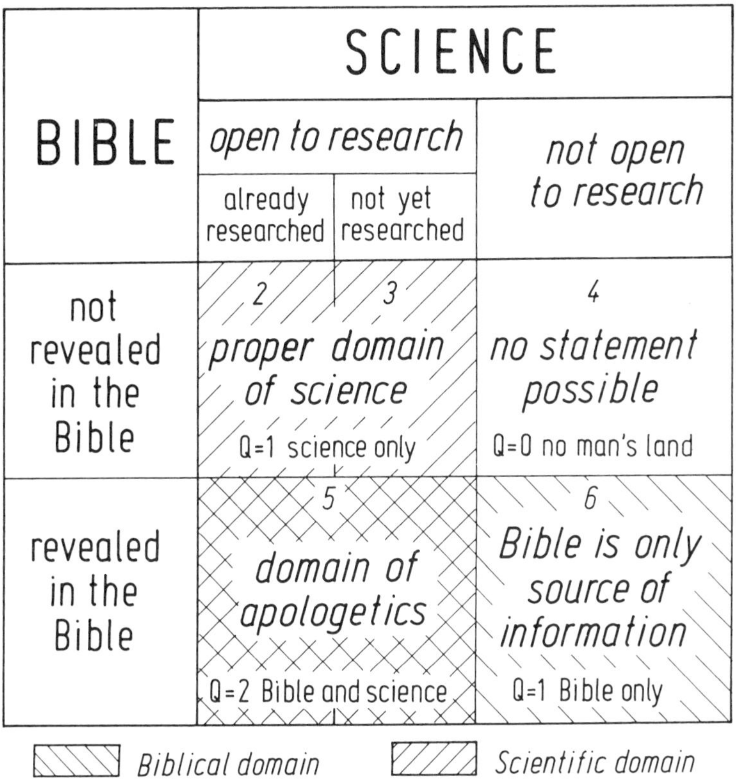

BIBLE	SCIENCE		
	open to research		*not open to research*
	already researched	not yet researched	
not revealed in the Bible	2 *proper domain of science* Q=1 science only	3	4 *no statement possible* Q=0 no man's land
revealed in the Bible	5 *domain of apologetics* Q=2 Bible and science		6 *Bible is only source of information* Q=1 Bible only

⬜ *Biblical domain*   ⬜ *Scientific domain*

what follows the main emphasis will be on the natural sciences, such as physics, chemistry, astronomy and biology.

1.5.1 False tracks in the field of science (region 1)
Before we examine region 2, the real area of scientific questions and enquiry, we must look at region 1, which one must always reckon with when human activity is involved. The state of humanity since the Fall is described in the Bible as a universal lostness: 'All we like sheep have gone astray' (Isa. 53:6). This scripture describes first and foremost the spiritual state of men who no longer have fellowship with God, but denotes further the essential fallibility of the human race, which includes the sciences man pursues. Writers of scientific

history have no choice but to include the chapters of illusion, error and fallacy. Many a time we have heard the words 'Science has proven. . .' revoked and replaced with an acknowledgement of mere speculation, unconscious error or even conscious deception. In Ernst Haeckel's day (1834-1919), his theory of the so-called 'biogenetic principle' was regarded as incontrovertible proof for evolution. Later the renowned biologist Adolf Portmann (1897-1983) said of this mistaken theory, 'We must not be deceived by the fact that these opinions come in the guise of scientific truth; they are derived from a personal belief.'

1.5.2 The proper area of science (region 2)

Right on the first page of the Bible we find God's command to man: 'Subdue the earth' (Gen. 1:28). This includes the discovery of animals and material aspects of the world God created. A deeper insight into the laws of creation leads to three results.

1. The more we appreciate the wonder of creation, the more we will praise God (Ps. 19; 104).
2. The more we understand creation, the better we can use it for the good of mankind (e.g. agriculture, technology, medicine).
3. The better our comprehension of the interaction of the various aspects of creation, the more responsibly we should treat them (no squandering of raw materials, environmental protection).

If the above list concerns primarily the natural sciences, similar aims may be set for other branches of science also. The depressing fact that scientific discoveries and methods may also be abused (e.g. the manufacture of atomic bombs, abuse of gene technology) does not discredit natural science as such. False applications and wrong directions (e.g. Marxism, 'God is dead' theology) are a result of the fall of man. The natural sciences offer us the means to discover those of nature's secrets which are accessible to us, but should not be used to provide a false authority for speculation in areas beyond human limits. The sciences, or rather their practitioners, are well advised to remain humble, because of man's intrinsic fallibility and the limited nature of scientific knowledge.

Scientific work is not done disinterestedly, without preconception. We will distinguish here two ways of doing science (research, teaching, application) which are fundamentally different from each other: one working according to the biblical spirit and one working from any other base (e.g. Greek philosophy, enlightenment, Marxism, humanism). The principles of biblical-oriented science are characterized as follows.

Service. It honours God and serves man. In the light of this knowledge the German study group *Wort und Wissen* has set itself a double task of service: on the one hand it aims to aid science and provide stimuli so that every theme of scientific research points to the Creator's work; on the other hand it aims to serve the body of Christ by showing that the Bible may be trusted in all situations. In particular, scientifically relevant details from the Bible and knowledge from the natural sciences can be treated as a whole, avoiding intellectual schizophrenia. For many people this recognition has meant liberation ('The truth will set you free' John 8:32); for them the Bible became once again or for the first time a source of strength, life information and thought.

Standard. God's Word is the standard and the rule. Not everything we are capable of doing is good for us.

Facts. Science which is followed according to biblical principles is realistic and takes into account all reliable observation of the natural world. As far as the publication of scientific results is concerned, there is no restriction whatsoever; all results may be freely discussed.

We can similarly consider the following three points for science not conducted according to biblical principles.

Service. This kind of science serves a philosophical or ideological system more often than we generally acknowledge (e.g. dialectical materialism, German physics in the Third Reich, evolutionary research).

Standard. 'Man is the measure of all things' (Protagoras). He is entirely autonomous and tolerates no imposed authority. Thus the only criteria for human activity are his will and his opinion. God delivered a twofold judgement on this arrogance at the building of the tower of Babel (Gen. 11:6-7):
1. the confusion of languages;
2. the confounding of human plans: 'Henceforth nothing that

they plan will be impossible for them' (Gen. 11:6).

The second sentence is even worse than the first, for it leaves the way clear for man to 'solve' even basic questions without God. Charles Darwin (1809-1882), Karl Marx (1818-1883) and Sigmund Freud (1856-1939) are the pioneers of science without an absolute standard. Its fruits have many names: imposed evolutionary thinking in almost all sciences, even including theology, a materialistic image of man in biology, medicine, psychology and society (in general), legalization of abortion.

Facts. Infiltration of science by ideology, going even as far as distorting and ignoring some of the facts.

1.5.3 Not yet researched (region 3)

The libraries of the world are filled with an unimaginable quantity of knowledge in the form of books and periodicals. At the present time there are about 50,000 different scientific periodicals. This mind-boggling flood of information should not blind us to the fact that the greater part of our potential knowledge is still waiting to be explored. The moon landing, for instance, threw up more questions and problems than it solved. A. Bierce rightly said, 'Knowledge is what we call that small part of ignorance which we have sorted and classified.'

Here are some examples from the plethora of unexplored questions.

1. Physicists are investing much effort to discover the structure of matter. The list of new particles is continually growing, but the stage of making hypothetical models has still not been passed.

2. The growth of biological structures is one of the hardest puzzles. How do the cells communicate with each other? How are cells joined to form organs of a specific size, and how do billions of cells form a constructional and functional unity? How is the information for the strictly functional system of blood vessels (100,000 km in a human being) stored? How is the blueprint for the eye determined?

3. The operation of the human brain is largely unknown. How is the circuit plan of this network, the most complicated construction known, genetically determined? What do consciousness, emotions and thought processes have to do with the brain?

In the light of the many open questions it is clear how few people know how much one needs to know to appreciate how little one knows! The philosopher Karl Popper once said, 'The saying of Socrates, "I know that I know nothing," is as relevant today as it was then, possibly even more so.' Our knowledge really is an island in an ocean of ignorance.

1.5.4 Fundamentally unresearchable, not revealed in the Bible (region 4)
There is a whole series of questions which are unanswerable in principle. Examples:

How many daughters did Adam and Eve have?

Which language did the first man speak?

What is the exact age of the earth?

What was the physiology of early mankind that made painless birth possible?

How extensive was the atmospheric envelope of water vapour before the Flood?

What kind of light was presented on the first creation day?

Where was the geographical position of Eden?

The Bible itself mentions areas barred from human research: '[God] does great things beyond understanding' (Job 9:10).

Just as in the macrocosmos there are secrets which cannot be unearthed, so there are similar questions relating to the microcosmos. Thus we can regard the Heisenberg Uncertainty Principle as a physically defined boundary between that which can be researched and that which cannot. Even in the most exact of all sciences, mathematics, there are theorems which in principle cannot be proven and problems which cannot be solved. Historical questions are basically unanswerable if there are no relevant records.

This region 4 contains a wealth of questions which belong in the scientific category, to which neither the Bible nor scientific methods give an answer. The founder of organic chemistry, Justus von Liebig (1803-1873) probably had this area in mind when he said, 'The point where science really begins to be interesting is where it stops.'

1.5.5 Open to science and revealed in the Bible (region 5)
This is the area of overlap of biblical revelation and scientific discovery, or in other words, where there is complementary

evidence for one and the same topic. This area is important
and significant for apologetics (Greek *apologia* = defence). We
have here the possibility of pointing out to people who have
not yet accepted the Bible as true the path of truth by selected
examples. When we find important scientific facts already
described in the Bible and realize they were written at a time
when the current world-view could not have produced them,
we perceive a clear indication of divine origin of information.
The Bible as a book of truth is independent of the state of
knowledge of that time but it is helpful to find natural science
confirming the Bible. We must not fall into the trap here of
interpreting and manipulating biblical statements until harmony is reached. Into the category of such forced harmoni-
zation would fall, for instance, all efforts to find theistic
evolution in the Bible. However, where natural science has
made certain assured discoveries both sources of knowledge
must arrive at the same conclusion although the knowledge
may be expressed in different ways.

The following language problems must be taken into
account when considering region 5, with its two independent
information sources.

1. **Scientific vocabulary.** In every branch of science one
finds specialized terms of reference which have arisen from a
refining process. Scientific vocabulary often uses words taken
from everyday language, which are then refined, given a
special meaning or redefined.

2. **Biblical vocabulary.** This very same pattern occurs in
biblical vocabulary: everyday terms or situations are taken
and given their own biblical meaning. Greek words like *kairos,
logos, kyrios, aeon, evangelios, ekklesia,* which were in common
usage, first took on their spiritual meanings in the Bible.
Hellenistic terms used by the Spirit of God for his service went
through a metamorphosis and were clothed with a new,
spiritual meaning. It would be fatal to try to interpret the
contents of the Bible using only the original worldly definitions of the words. The error of universalism stems from
limiting the biblical meaning of a single word. According to
this theory the word *'aeon'* is seen exclusively as a certain
period of time, as the Greeks normally used it. But the New
Testament clearly uses the word in connection with eternity
(e.g. John 6:51, Rev. 11:15), giving it a much more far-
reaching significance.

3. **Modern scientific statements** which the Bible contains are not expressed in the scientific terminology of today; sometimes circumlocutions and pictures are necessary if the matter is to be described correctly. When Amos (9:2) and Obadiah wrote, they knew nothing of satellites, space labs, orbital station or space shuttles, but what they wrote under God applies to the space programme of our time: 'Though you soar aloft like the eagle, though your nest is set among the stars, thence I will bring you down, says the Lord' (Obad. 4).

4. **Phenomenological speech.** In the Bible, as in the linguistic usage of today's science, our language is often phenomenological, i.e. we often describe only the appearance, not the state of affairs underlying it. Thus every modern astronomer talks, as the Bible does, of sunrise and sunset, although these phenomena arise from the earth's rotation, not the 'course of the sun'.

5. **Particular modes of speech.** Every language has various forms of expression at its disposal; thus idioms, figurative and poetic speech contribute to the richness of a language, i.e. they serve both aesthetic purposes and to describe a situation more exactly; in the same way the Bible makes use of every linguistic refinement to present its message in the most comprehensible form.

1.5.6 Revealed in the Bible, not open to scientific research (region 6)
We now come to another area where biblical revelation and scientific questions have common ground. The difference in comparison with region 5 is, however, that the subjects of discussion here are, as in region 4, not open to any kind of experiment; in contrast to 4, however, we are fortunate enough to have a reliable source of information at our disposal — the Bible! However, the fact that apart from the Bible there is no other reliable source of information in this region has not prevented people from thinking about such questions — on the contrary, the libraries of the world and men's thoughts are full of attempts to answer just these questions. The biologist P. Sitte nevertheless correctly and very significantly points out: 'We live in a world which we cannot comprehend... we scientists cannot make a study of that which is not susceptible to our methods: woe to the man who does not know his limits.'[3]

We will now list some examples of questions belonging to region 6, a fascinating area for our subject.

1. **Cosmogonical questions — questions of origins.** All human attempts to find answers in this realm, whether by philosophy, religion or science, demonstrate convincingly human inability to produce a conclusive answer. No one was present to witness the beginning of the universe or of life and so no one can tell us about it. Therefore only the Creator himself can give us the information we need.

2. **Cosmological questions.** What is the structure of the universe? Is it finite or infinite, bounded or unbounded, or is it finite but unbounded? The Bible answers these questions only by saying that the general structure of the universe cannot be mapped out by mankind (Jer. 31:37).

3. **Length of the days of creation.** All argument about this question is pointless, since there is here also only one source of information, namely the account of creation in Genesis 1. The author has dealt with this topic extensively and discussed it in detail elsewhere.[4]

4. **The temporal bounds of the universe.** Does our world have an end in time or not? Futurologists and Marxists alike occupy themselves with this question. An infinitely long timespan for our universe does not fit into the system of ideas propounded by dialectic Marxism. But only the living God, who created the world and in whose hand it rests, can give us the definitive answer. That the world will perish is shown by many sayings in the Bible, e.g. Matthew 24:35; Psalm 102:26-27; Isaiah 50:9; Romans 8:20; 1 Corinthians 7:31; 2 Peter 3:10; Revelation 20:11. The end will not be caused by a cosmic catastrophe such as the impact of a meteorite or 'collision with the stars', nor by a nuclear disaster caused by mankind, but by the direct intervention of God.

5. **The diurnal cycle.** Is the familiar cycle of day and night permanent? Astronomers have calculated that after several thousand million years the earth's rotation will have been reduced so much by tidal friction that day and night will last several (current) months. But that would mean that no plant could survive, since the conditions necessary for plant growth would no longer be present. This is also a godless calculation, since he has promised: 'As long as the earth remains, seedtime and harvest, cold and heat, summer and winter, day and night

should not cease' (Gen. 8:22). Up to the last day of the history of the world seedtime and harvest will be possible, so that the present conditions, such as the length of day and night, will also be fulfilled.

God was grieved by human behaviour before the Flood: 'Man will no longer be ruled (corrected, taught) by my spirit' (Gen. 6:3, possible reading), and our age is condemned by Jesus in the same way as Noah's was (Matt. 24:37-39). Man's philosophy is given more weight than God's Word, so that we are looking in the wrong place, as God accuses us of doing in Jeremiah 2:13: 'They have forsaken me, the fountain of living waters, and hewed out cisterns for themselves, broken cisterns that can hold no water.' For region 6 there is only one source (Ps. 36:9). If we seek water (= information) anywhere else we will come upon mud, decay or poison (= misinformation). The common practice of today is like a man looking for his lost key under a street lamp at night. When asked if he knew that he had left his key in the place where he was looking for it he replied, 'No, but at least I can see here.'

1.6 The Bible's own testimony

God has spoken to us in many different ways and informed us of the meaning, the claim to truth and the result of accepting or rejecting his Word. Some selected testimonies to this will help us here.

1.6.1 The testimony of the Old Testament

Several Old Testament references make it clear to us that we are not dealing with words of human wisdom, but rather with claims bearing the seal of truth and the authority of the living God. The Old Testament contains 3,808 different expressions of confirmation that it has recorded God's own words. For example:

'God is not a man, that he should lie. . .
Does he speak and then not act?
Does he promise and not fulfil?' (Num. 23:19).
'Your statutes stand firm' (Ps. 93:5).
'All your words are true' (Ps. 119:160).
'Every word of God is flawless' (Prov. 30:5).
'Now, I have put my words in your mouth' (Jer. 1:9).

'This is the word that came to Jeremiah from the Lord'
(Jer. 7:1).
'The word of the Lord came to me. . .' (Ezek. 7:1).

1.6.2 The testimony of the apostle Paul

Paul was the chosen instrument of God (Acts 9:15) whom the
Lord used and enabled, in a very special way, to bring the
divine message to the world. His testimony to the Scripture is
therefore a binding and lasting criterion for us also.

The writers of the Bible did not record what they absorbed
from the Greeks or Babylonians or from contemporary trends,
but were conveyers of the truth which no man could invent, in
obedience to God and led by the Holy Spirit: 'We had to speak
the word of God to you first. Since you reject it and do not
consider yourselves worthy of eternal life, we now turn to the
Gentiles' (Acts 13:46).

'I did not receive it from any man, nor was I taught it;
rather, I received it by revelation from Jesus Christ' (Gal.
1:12).

'All Scripture is God-breathed and is useful for teaching,
rebuking, correcting and training in righteousness' (2 Tim.
3:16).

1.6.3 The testimony of the apostle Peter

'For prophecy never had its origin in the will of man, but men
spoke from God as they were carried along by the Holy Spirit'
(2 Peter 1:21).

1.6.4 The testimony of Jesus Christ

On the mountain of transfiguration God's voice was heard:
'This is my beloved Son, with whom I am well pleased; listen
to him' (Matt 17:5). In these last days God has spoken to us
through Jesus (Heb. 1:1-2). It is to his Word we must listen to
keep us from falling prey to error. Jesus is the truth
personified. His attitude to Scripture makes him the crowning
witness to its truth.

God attests and guarantees Jesus' authority. The Lord
Jesus was able to say, 'I and the Father are one' (John 10:30).
Jesus and the Word of God complement each other's
authority so that they merge into one authoritative source of
truth. What an incomparable source of information we have
in the Scriptures!

'Have you never read in the Scriptures?' (Matt. 21:42).
(To the Sadducees): 'You are in error because you do not know the Scriptures or the power of God' (Matt. 22:29).
'Heaven and earth will pass away, but my words will never pass away' (Matt. 24:35).
'But this has all taken place that the writings of the prophets might be fulfilled' (Matt. 26:56).
'They have Moses and the Prophets; let them listen to them. . . If they do not listen to Moses and the Prophets, they will not be convinced even if someone rises from the dead' (Luke 16:29-31).
'But since you do not believe what he [Moses] wrote, how are you going to believe what I say?' (John 5:47).
'He who belongs to God hears what God says. The reason you do not hear is that you do not belong to God' (John 8:47).
'The Scripture cannot be broken' (John 10:35).
'If anyone loves me, he will obey my teaching' (John 14:23).
'You are already clean because of the word I have spoken to you' (John 15:3).
Jesus prays to the Father after his work (John 17):
'For I gave them the words you gave me and they accepted them' (v. 8).
'I have given them your word' (v. 14).
'Sanctify them by the truth; your word is truth' (v. 17).

2. The creation narrative

The biblical creation narrative is an indispensable and irreplaceable source of information when we are looking for the origin and purpose of this world and life itself. We can see from a closer look at Genesis 1 and 2 that besides a wealth of statements of faith there are scientific ones too. The following aims to select some of the most relevant points. (By 'scientific statements' we mean those which have relevance to natural science.) Notice how divine revelation lays bare the error in current human evolutionary theory. Various teachings and statements in the New Testament (e.g. Matt. 12:40; 19:4-6; 1 Cor. 11:8-9; 15:44-45; 1 Tim. 2:11-14) have their roots in the

Old Testament, especially in the creation narrative (see Fig. 4).

2.1 Scientific statements in the creation narrative

1. Space, time and matter are not eternal, but have had a definite beginning (Gen. 1:1).

2. The earth did not begin as an incandescent fireball, but was created from the beginning with a surface covered with water (Gen. 1:2).

3. The earth and the other heavenly bodies do not originate from a universal big bang, but were created separately on different (the first and fourth) days of creation.

4. The earth is — according not to its position in space but to God's creative purpose — the central heavenly body. The function of the other bodies (planets, sun, moon, stars) is only to serve mankind (Gen. 1:14 — measurement of time and determination of the calendar) and to point to the Creator (Ps. 19; Rom. 1:20).

5. The earth did not start with a reducing atmosphere of methane, hydrogen and ammonia, which developed over thousands of millions of years into the present-day oxidizing atmosphere; rather, an oxygen-rich atmosphere, perfectly suited for the animal and plant world and for human beings, was created on the second day.

6. Life did not evolve starting in water; it was created on land: on the third day God created vegetation (Gen. 1:11,12).

7. The first animals were not primitive, low forms of life but distinct species of fish, birds and large sea animals. Whales — highly developed mammals — were among the first animals (Gen. 1:20-21).

8. Birds did not develop from reptiles: they were created a whole creation day before the creeping animals (Gen. 1:20, 24-25).

9. The first animals of the creation were plant-eating; only after the Fall did they become carnivores (Gen. 1:30).

10. Man has no animal ancestors; he was created separately (Gen. 1:27).

11. The language of man did not develop from primitive noises from the animal world. The gift of articulate speech with the ability to converse and create words was his from the beginning (Gen. 2:19-20, 23;2:9-13).

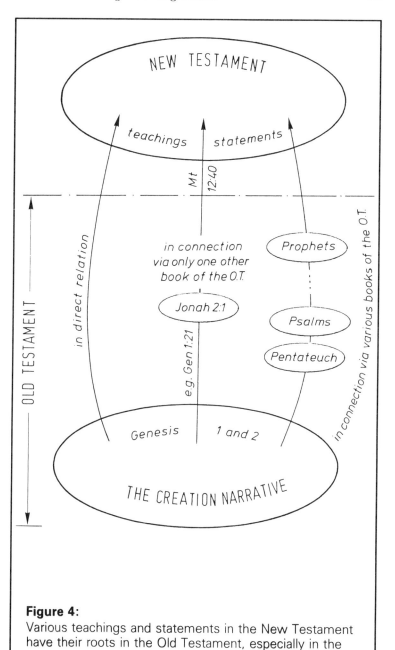

Figure 4:
Various teachings and statements in the New Testament have their roots in the Old Testament, especially in the creation narrative.

12. The world did not evolve over some thousands of millions of years but was created in six normal twenty-four-hour days.

2.2 Statements of faith in the creation narrative

1. God is the Creator of the world and of all life (Gen. 1:1). The Holy Spirit also took part in creation. The work of creation was carried out by Jesus Christ (Col. 1:15-16; John 1:1-4,10). He is the Word, without whom nothing that exists was made (John 1:3).

2. God's methods of creation are: through the word (the phrase 'and God said' occurs ten times in Gen. 1); by power (Jer. 10:12); by wisdom (Prov. 3:19); by his will (Rev. 4:11); spontaneously (Ps. 33:9) and out of nothing (*ex nihilo*) (Heb. 11:3).

3. Man was created in God's image (Gen. 1:27). At his creation he received his spirit when God breathed into him. His threefold constitution of spirit, soul and body (1 Thess. 5:23) makes man different from animals not merely in details but fundamentally. God assigned man such a high place that he was created 'only a little lower than God' (Ps. 8:5).

4. The man was created first; the woman was then created by God from the man's rib and given to him as a helper (Gen. 2:18, 21-22).

5. Marriage is not an invention of man during some stage in his cultural development but was established by God for the first couple (Gen. 2:24).

6. The first human couple lived in the Garden of Eden until the Fall. Eden was not a mythical or allegorical term but a real place.

7. God gave man dominion over the earth and the animal world — but not over other people! (Gen. 1:28; Ps. 8:7.)

8. The possibility of extraterrestrial life must be ruled out because of the special role God intended for the earth.

9. God's pronouncement on his completed creation was 'very good'! Thus there was no toil, illness, death, suffering or pain in the whole creation before the Fall.

10.After the six days of creation God rested on the seventh day and hallowed it. In the Sinai commandments (Exod. 20:9-11) this work-cycle is also given to mankind.

2.3 What is the biblical creation narrative?

A. Human answers:

It is of vital importance how we read the creation narrative
and what significance we attach to it; hardly any other part of
the Bible has been so caught in the cross-fire of man's
criticism. Consequently many people perceive only a distorted
and misplaced idea of the divine information. In what follows
we will present various human answers derived from this
process of relativizing. To conclude we give the divine answer
which follows from the testimony in section 1.6.

1. A text which was written down after a long verbal
tradition.

2. One which was the result of a long evolutionary literary
process.

3. An antiquated text from past centuries.

4. A mythical tale.

5. An edited summary from different sources (priestly
writings, Jahwist).

6. A retrospective justification of the sabbath command-
ment.

7. A traditional view of the beginning of the world.

8. A testimony of faith by the people of Israel.

9. A hymn to the Creator.

10. A conception of the universe, now scientifically out-of-
date.

11. A collection of prophetic picture-language writings.

12. A story of the origin of this world which is not meant to
be taken literally, but which corresponded to man's understanding at the time.

13. A collection of beliefs about the creation.

14. A profession of faith in God as Creator, which, however,
is not intended to convey any scientific facts.

15. A Jewish tale about the creation whose content was
influenced by other, even older myths.

16. A creation story which accommodates our modern
evolutionary theories without difficulty.

17. One of many creation theories which the cultures of that
time produced.

B. God's answer
The biblical creation narrative is information from God with
the seal of absolute truth.

It is therefore a report of facts and is to be taken literally.
It contains essential statements of faith.
It contains basic scientific facts which make up an
indispensable framework for any research which is to
correspond with reality.

The biblical creation narrative is thus a denial of:
all other conceptions of creation that man has produced;
all philosophical models of the origin of the universe;
all models of origins involving evolution.

Consequence: Either the biblical creation narrative has a
purely human origin — whereupon it is as meaningless as the
Edda — or it is authorized by God and therefore completely
binding.

3. Creation: examples of the wisdom of the Creator

*3.1 From the patent office of the Creator: The flight of migratory
birds*
The Bible reveals to us various principles which God used in
the creation: through the word, by will, from nothing *(ex
nihilo)*, spontaneously, through Jesus Christ. Let us examine
one aspect, which is spoken of in Psalm 104:24: 'O Lord, how
manifold are your works! In wisdom you have made them all;
the earth is full of your creatures.' We encounter these works,
so wisely conceived, at every turn. We shall consider just one
particular example here and that is the flight of migratory
birds.[5] If we take a closer look at this phenomenon we
encounter two miracles: energy and navigation.

3.1.1 The miracle of energy
Every process, whether in physics, technology or biology,
adheres strictly to the law of conservation of energy. That is to
say, any work to be done requires a certain amount of energy
to be supplied. The problem facing the migratory bird is that
of taking with it sufficient fuel (= fat) to complete its journey.
To ensure the necessary flying capacity the bird must be of as

light a build as possible; excess weight is to be avoided at all costs. Likewise use of fuel has to be as efficient as possible. How then did the Creator make the fuel last so long without refilling? The first step is choosing the most economical cruising speed. Should the bird fly too slowly, it would consume too much fuel simply to stay airborne. If it flies too quickly, it wastes too much energy in overcoming air resistance. Thus we see that there is a definite optimum for the consumption of fuel. If the bird knew about this speed, it would be able to fly as efficiently as possible. Depending on the aerodynamic construction of the rump and wings the optimal speed is different for each bird (e.g. laughing gull 45 km/h; budgerigar 41.6 km/h). It is a known fact that birds gear themselves exactly to this energy-saving speed. How do they know? It is one of many unsolved ornithological puzzles.

We want to examine more closely the energy problem of the golden plover (*pluvialis dominica fulva*). This bird migrates from Alaska to Hawaii for the winter. Its non-stop flight takes it across the open sea where there is no island *en route*; in addition the bird cannot swim, so that a stop for rest is impossible. This flight of over 4,000 km (depending on its starting-point) involves an incredible 250,000 consecutive wing beats and lasts 88 hours. The bird's starting weight is $G_0 = 200$ g, of which 70 g is stored as layers of fat to be used as fuel. It is known that the golden plover converts 0.6% per hour of its current body weight ($p = 0.006/h$) into kinetic energy and heat. For the first hour of flight it therefore needs

$$x_1 = G_0 \cdot p = 200 \times 0.006 = 1.2 \text{ grams of fat.} \tag{1}$$

Thus at the beginning of the second hour it weighs only $G_0 - x_1 = 200 - 1.2 = 198.8$ g, so that it uses slightly less fat for the second hour:

$$x_2 = (G_0 - x_1) \cdot p = G_1 \cdot p = 198.8 \times 0.006 = 1.193 \text{ g} \tag{2}$$
$$x_3 = (G_0 - x_1 - x_2) \cdot p = G_2 \cdot p = 197.6 \times 0.006 = 1.186 \text{ g} \tag{3}$$

and for the 88th hour of flight the fuel consumption has fallen to

$$x_{88} = (G_0 - x_1 - x_2 - x_3 - \dots - x_{87}) \cdot p = G_{87} \cdot p \tag{4}$$

Now we will calculate how much the bird weighs at the end of the flight. Its body weight at the end of each hour is given by the reduction due to the fat consumption:

1st hour: $\quad G_1 = G_0 - x_1 = G_0 - G_0 \cdot p = G_0 \cdot (1-p)$ $\qquad$ (5)

2nd hour: $\quad G_2 = G_1 - x_2 = G_1 - G_1 \cdot p = G_1 \cdot (1-p) =$
$\qquad\qquad G_0 \cdot (1-p)^2$ $\qquad\qquad\qquad\qquad\qquad\qquad$ (6)

3rd hour: $\quad G_3 = G_2 - x_3 = G_2 - G_2 \cdot p = G_2 \cdot (1-p) =$
$\qquad\qquad G_0 \cdot (1-p)^3$ $\qquad\qquad\qquad\qquad\qquad\qquad$ (7)
$\qquad\qquad \downarrow$

mth hour: $\quad G_m = G_{m-1} - x_m = G_{m-1} - G_{m-1} \cdot p =$
$\qquad\qquad G_{m-1} \cdot (1-p) = G_0 \cdot (1-p)^m$ $\qquad\qquad$ (8)
$\qquad\qquad \downarrow$

88th hour: $\quad G_{88} = G_{87} - x_{88} = G_{87} - G_{87} \cdot p =$
$\qquad\qquad G_{87} \cdot (1-p) = G_0 \cdot (1-p)^{88}$ $\qquad\qquad$ (9)

According to this simple method* the individual weights G_0, G_1, G_2 ..., G_{88} form a geometrical sequence with multiplication factor $q = 1-p < 1$. If we put in the figures for equation 9, the bird's weight after the 88th hour is given by

$$G_{88} = 200 \cdot (1 - 0.006)^{88} = 117.8 \, \text{g}. \tag{10}$$

The total fuel consumption is then the difference from the initial weight:

$$G_0 - G_{88} = 200 - 117.8 = 82.2 \, \text{g} \tag{11}$$

This value is distinctly more than the available 70 g! The bird may not go below the limit of 130 g (Fig. 5). In spite of flying at the speed which minimizes his fuel consumption the bird has not enough fuel to reach Hawaii. To find the number of hours that the fuel is sufficient for, we find using

$$G_z = G_0 (1-p)^z = 200 - 70 = 130 \, \text{g}$$

(*) For the sake of simplicity we have performed the above calculation in steps of 1 hour; we could, however, have used the differential equation $dG/dt = -G(t) \cdot p$ with $G(t=0) = G_0$, giving the solution $G = G_0 \cdot \exp(-p \cdot t)$ with $p = 0.006/h$, but the discrete method differs negligibly (0.1%) from the exact solution.

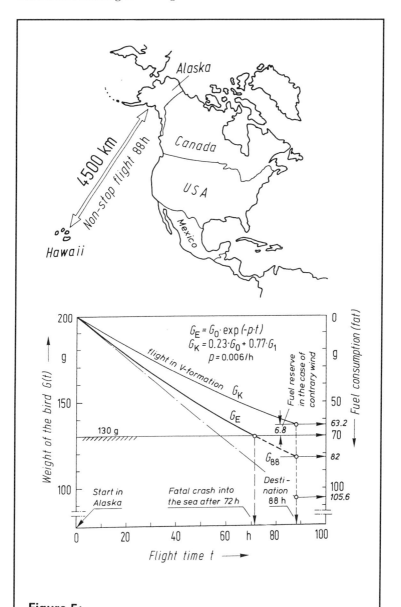

Figure 5:
Illustration of the flight of the golden plover from Alaska to Hawaii (geographical route, curves of the fuel consumption during the bird's flight).

that the 70 g of fat are used up after $z = 72$ hours, which means that after 81% of the projected time, i.e. a good 800 km before the end, the bird crashes into the sea. Have we miscalculated, or has the Creator not, as we thought, designed and equipped the bird properly? Neither: the Creator's work leaves us gaping. The clue is the motto 'optimal use of energy through information'. He gave the bird an important piece of information as well: 'Do not fly singly (Fig. 5, curve G_F) but in V-formation (curve G_K). In V-formation you will save 23% of your energy and reach your winter quarters safely.' Figure 5 also shows the curve G_K, the rate of weight loss when flying in V-formation. After 88 hours this would normally leave 6.8 g of fat in hand; this remaining fuel reserve is not superfluous, however, but has been included by the Creator so that the bird reaches its goal even with a contrary wind. The extremely low fuel consumption of $p = 0.6\%$ of the total weight per hour is even more astonishing when one considers that the corresponding values for man-made mechanical flying machines are many times larger (helicopter $p = 4$-5%, jet $p = 12\%$).

For anyone who does not regard these finely adjusted processes as the work of a Creator the following questions remain unanswered:

How does the bird know how much fat is necessary?

How does it arrange to have this amount just before the journey?

How does the bird know the distance and the specific rate of fuel consumption?

How does the bird know the way?

How does it navigate?

As well as the aforementioned (East Siberian) golden plover there is also the North American golden plover. This also flies in a dazzling nonstop performance straight across the Atlantic Ocean from the coasts of Labrador to North Brazil. Whereas the western breed flies the same course for both journeys the North American golden plover chooses different routes for autumn and spring. The return flight from the pampas of South America crosses Central America and the United States to Canada. The following equally incredible flight perform-ances are recorded for:

— the Japanese snipe (*Capella hardtwickii*): 5,000 km flight from Japan to Tasmania
— the needle-tailed swift of Eastern Siberia (*Chaetura caudacuta*): flight from Siberia to Tasmania
— the American sandpiper (e.g. *Calidris melanotos* = pectoral sandpiper): 16,000 km flight from Alaska to Terra del Fuego.

3.1.2 The navigational miracle
The famous Danish ornithologist Finn Salomonsen has this to say about a bird's orientation during migration: 'The bird's ability to find its way during migration is surely the greatest mystery. Seldom has another question given so much cause for theorizing and speculation as this one.'[6] Indeed this navigational achievement, performed without complex boards of instruments, compass and map and under constantly changing conditions including sun position, wind direction, cloud cover and the diurnal cycle, is an incomparable miracle. Even a slight diversion off course while crossing the ocean would mean certain death in the open sea for migrating land birds, as we discovered in the case of the golden plover. Keeping exactly on course is not a question of trial and error. The vast majority of migrating birds would never reach their destination without navigational methods, and no species could survive such an overwhelming loss rate; thus any suggestion that evolution has played a part here must be totally dismissed. Also the suggestion that young birds learn the way flying with their parents carries little weight, as many species fly solo. It is thought then that migratory birds have an instinctive sense of direction like a compass, which makes it possible for them to orientate themselves and thus keep flying in a certain direction. Salomonsen bases his theory about the sense of direction on his study of two kinds of small bird from West Greenland, both of which fly south in autumn. The stonechat (*Saxicola torquata*) and the snow bunting (*Plectrophenax nivalis*) share a common homeground and often begin their southward journey at the same time. Once the south of Greenland is reached, however, their ways separate: whereas the snow bunting continues his journey southwards to winter in America, the stonechat turns south-east to follow a course over the Atlantic to Western Europe and North Africa. Each

bird has a specific sense of direction which determines its migration pattern.

Displacement experiments have been carried out with various migratory birds which showed detailed results about the precision of their navigational capabilities: a most remarkable test involving two species of tern (*Sterna fuscata* and *Anous stolidus*) and their nesting places in the Tortugas Islands in the Gulf of Mexico was one such experiment. The birds were shipped in different directions and set free on the open sea. Although they were freed at distances ranging from 832 to 1368 km from their nests over parts of the sea which were completely unfamiliar to them, within a few days most of the terns returned almost directly to their eggs and young on the Tortugas Islands. The longest disorientation experiment carried out to date was probably one involving a manx shearwater (*Puffinus puffinus*) which was taken from its nest on Skokholm Island in Wales to Boston, U.S.A. It arrived back at its nest in 12 days, 12 hours and 31 minutes after a 5,000 km nonstop transatlantic flight. A large number of disorientation experiments have been carried out on homing pigeons in particular, and it is their navigational achievements which have been most thoroughly researched and documented. Salomonsen, writing about this breathtaking navigational feat, says, 'Even when birds were anaesthetized for the outward journey, or if their cage was made to rotate continuously so that its orientation was constantly changing, they were just as able to find their way home as were the control birds. Therefore there can be no doubt that birds have a special sense of geographical position, i.e. a real navigational sense. The nature of this instinct remains a mystery; even more so, the location of the relevant sense organ.'[7]

The birds' capabilities extend beyond the bounds of our imagination. They can determine their homeward course over long distances, even when all possible aids to orientation have been removed during the disorientation journey. They possess the extraordinary faculty of being able, wherever they are, to determine their position relative to their home territory from their immediate surroundings. And this method of determining location, itself not understood even today, is only the beginning; then comes the real problem, namely flight navigation: mere sense of direction is not enough for this.

During flight over wide, windswept stretches of ocean, a tendency to drift off course cannot be avoided; such drift must continually be compensated for, as in a feedback system in control technology, in order to avoid losing energy by flying a longer route. The Creator equipped the birds with a precise 'autopilot' which apparently is constantly measuring its geographical position and comparing these data with its individually 'programmed' destination. In this way an economical, energy-saving and direct flight is guaranteed. Just where this vital system is to be found and how this operating information is coded is known by no one today except the Creator, who made it.

3.2 Information density in the living cells
For our second example of God's perfection in design we turn to the living cell.

A masterpiece in miniaturizing storage and reproduction of information becomes apparent in such cells. The biological systems are ordered to such a high degree that any possibility that these systems developed by chance must be totally excluded. In the DNA molecule information is compressed to the unbelievably high density of 10^{21}bit/cm^3.[8] In information theory the smallest unit of information is called a bit. Especially in binary-coded notations the bit has two possible values: 'zero' or 'one'. In comparing the figures just mentioned to a computer's density of information, which amounts to about 10^3–10^4bit/cm^3 (in microprocessors 10^6–10^7bit/cm^3) it is easy to realize what an astronomical range separates them. The same difference results if the total surface of the earth is compared to the surface of a relatively small chestnut!

A further comparison will demonstrate the miracle of information storage miniaturization. Nowadays, more scientists are living than ever before since the beginning of the world. Every six minutes, a new book is published in the Federal Republic of Germany. Every two seconds, a scientific publication is issued throughout the world. We face a vast flood of information. The total knowledge in the world collected in books is known to be about 10^{16}, at the utmost 10^{17} bits. The same giant amount of information could be stored in 0.00001 cm^3 or one hundredth mm^3 of genetic material. In the genetic material of DNA molecules we

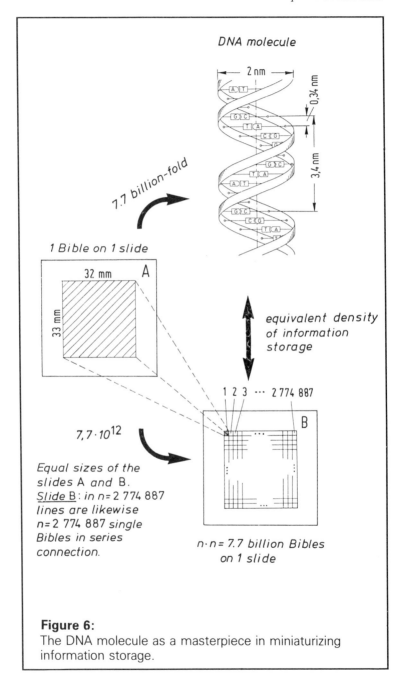

Figure 6:
The DNA molecule as a masterpiece in miniaturizing
information storage.

encounter the greatest known storage density of information. In Figure 6 we find graphical comparison[9] of the information densities between the DNA molecules and a special slide with the whole Bible (= smallest Bible in the world). In view of such facts, we cannot but join the psalmist's prayer: 'Open my eyes that I may see wonderful things in your law'! (Ps. 119:18.) How right was the famous French mathematician, Blaise Pascal (1623-1662), in saying, 'As all things tell of God to those who know him, and reveal him to those who love him, likewise they conceal him from all those who do not search for him and know him'!

References

1. Gitt, W., *Denken, glauben, leben — Technik, Religion, Evangelium —* Reihe WISSEN UND LEBEN, Band 3, Hänssler-Verlag, Neuhausen — Stuttgart, 1982, p.111.
2. Willner, H., *Schöpfung*, Zum Beispiel (1971), (Magazine for the Practice of Christian Education in School and Church.), Verlag die Spur, pp.119-143.
3. Sitte, P., *Unterwegs zu einem Weltbild der Naturwissenschaften* Naturwissenschaften 66 (1979), pp.273-278.
4. Gitt, W., *Das biblische Zeugnis der Schöpfung*, Reihe WISSEN UND LEBEN, Band 4, Hänssler-Verlag, Neuhausen — Stuttgart, 1983, p.190.
5. Dröscher, V.B., *Überlebensformel*, dtv-Taschenbuch, 2nd edition 1982, p.329.
   Rüppell, G., *Vogelflug*, Rowohlt Taschenbuch Verlag GmbH, 1980, p.209.
   Salomonsen, F., *Vogelzug*, From the series: *Moderne Biologie* BLV Munich, Basel, Vienna, 1969, p.210.
6. Salomonsen, F., *op.cit.*
7. *Idem.*
8. Gitt, W., *Am Anfang war die Information — Forschungsergebnisse der Naturwissenschaft und Technik —* Resch-Verlag, Gräfelfing/Munich, 1982, p.211; also *Das biblische Zeugnis der Schöpfung*.
9. Gitt. W., *Das biblische Zeugnis der Schöpfung*.

2.

Biblical creationism and scientific creationism — is there a conflict?

E.H. Andrews

I want to address the two aspects of our subject in turn. That is, I intend to look firstly at scientific creationism and secondly at biblical creationism. I want us to see their separate natures and purposes and to consider whether these can be reconciled with one another. But before we begin it might be useful, by way of introduction, to remind ourselves that creationism is not to be equated with Christianity. In our enthusiasm for creationism we sometimes forget that creationism does not have a one-to-one relationship with the Christian faith. There were Jewish creationists long before there were Christian creationists. There were Babylonian creationists at a very early date, although the Babylonian view of origins was very different from the Christian one. Indeed, any religion that incorporates a creation myth or story, in which origins are ascribed to metaphysical or supernatural causes, is by definition creationist in character.

So there have always been non-Christian creationists and this is still the situation today. I certainly do not consider the Jehovah's Witnesses to be Christians, but they are nevertheless avid creationists. I know Buddhists who are creationists. I even know agnostics who are creationists, though that may appear to be a contradiction in terms. Creationism, therefore, is not identical to Christianity. I mention this so that we shall be on our guard, when advocating creationist arguments, to be sure that we are doing what we want to do; to be sure that we are promulgating the truth as it is in Christ, and not something alien to the Christian gospel.

Scientific creationism

There is today a phenomenon in which we not only have Christian creationists and non-Christian creationists, but also Bible-believing Christians who advance a non-biblical or a-biblical creationism. They are quite deliberately leaving aside the biblical revelation and attempting to establish the fact of creation by the use of scientific methodology. This is not a new phenomenon since the natural theologians of earlier years were trying to accomplish the very same thing. Some of those we honour as the fathers of modern science adopted essentially this position of scientific creationism, though they did not, of course, employ that term. They tried to provide evidence for the existence of God, and in support of the Christian faith, from an examination of nature. One of Isaac Newton's most famous quotations is as follows: 'When I wrote my treatise about our system, I had an eye upon such principles as might work with considering men for the belief of a Deity.'[1]

Now that is an excellent summary of natural theology. If discoveries in, and contemplations of, nature can persuade men to believe in God on an intellectual level, then natural theology is valid. It means that revelation is not essential to this formative step of coming to a belief in God. In this context we should perhaps remember that Newton himself was a unitarian; he was not a trinitarian believer because he found the biblical doctrine of the Trinity unacceptable to reason. Reason rather than revelation was his touchstone, and this is wholly consistent with the approach of natural theology. It seems to me, then, that this situation, in which we find Bible-believing Christians promoting an extra-biblical creationism, has come to the fore again in our day, and this is what I want to address.

We are aware, I think, of the reasons why some of our American colleagues have adopted this line. The American constitution forbids the teaching of religion in the public (or state) schools. This provision was originally introduced to protect religious minorities, but it is being used today to exclude religious teaching from the schools, while permitting atheistic philosophies to be taught under the guise of science. In a very natural desire to resist and oppose the naturalistic teaching of evolution, American Christians have reintroduced the concept of scientific creationism.

Let us define our terms. By scientific creationism I mean 'a belief in creation induced by scientific methodology without reference to revelation'. Biblical creationism, on the other hand, I define as 'a belief in creation based upon revelation (Scripture)'.

It will be helpful to talk about the purpose of scientific creationism. Its purpose, according to its authors, is to establish a creation model of origins by appeal only to scientific facts and arguments, and to the exclusion of all biblical evidence or belief. Having established a creation model on scientific grounds, they hope that men will be predisposed to receive the biblical testimony on creation, and on other topics like salvation, because the errors of evolution have been swept aside. This is the strategy of scientific creationism.

The question I want to ask of scientific creationism is whether it is actually able to secure those objectives. I am going to suggest that it is not capable of doing so, and I want to give you my reasons for that opinion in what follows.

The first reason for saying that scientific creationism fails in its declared purpose is that the supposed symmetry, or balance, between the creation model, on one hand, and the evolutionary model, on the other hand, is illusory. Let me explain. The idea is that you have an evolutionary model of origins and one needs to set up, as an alternative scenario, a creation model. Then by scientific arguments and obser-vation, one can take these two models and compare their respective predictions or implications, and thus arrive at a conclusion as to which model is more likely to be correct.

However, it seems to me that the implied symmetry between the two models does not exist. Look firstly at evolutionary theory. This is a positive attempt to discover natural processes occurring today that are sufficient to explain origins — to account for the origin of the universe, the origin of life, the origin of species, the origin of man. Evolution is therefore a positive attempt to discover such processes of natural law without any appeal to discontinuities or divine intervention. We may believe that this attempt is mistaken and bound to fail. Nevertheless it is a positive endeavour to establish the model in question.

When we come to scientific creationism, we find a completely different situation. For scientific creationism is an essentially negative statement. That may surprise some of you and alarm others, but let me explain what I mean. Scientific creationism firstly attacks evolutionary theory. This is a legitimate role, and in my view the only legitimate role, for scientific creationism. That is to say, it is perfectly proper that we should oppose evolution on scientific grounds. We should point out how evolutionary theory fails to account for the facts, and in what respects it is inadequate; to what extent it extrapolates the present into the past to an unacceptable degree; we should expose it as a philosophical rather than a scientific theory and so on. But this is all essentially negative.

For one reason or another we may be able to demonstrate that some particular theory of evolution is false. But scientific creationism suffers from one great defect. It can only attack evolutionary theory point by point. It may destroy the Lamarckian theory, for example, by scientific reasoning. Lamarckians respond with the neo-Lamarckian theory which is today enjoying something of a vogue. We may feel that neo-Darwinian theory is beginning to totter under scientific criticism. Indeed, there are now a significant number of scientists who see that neo-Darwinian theory is inadequate. But no sooner does one dismiss one particular theory of evolution than another one emerges. Thus we now have the theory of punctuated equilibrium which avoids some of the scientific criticisms levelled at neo-Darwinianism. It has its own weaknesses, of course, but it serves to illustrate my point that as soon as one enemy has been destroyed, another rises to take its place. Through all of this the fabric of evolution is not in fact damaged. Specific mechanisms may be banished, but the essential structure, the fabric, of evolutionary thinking remains intact. Thus a purely negative attack upon evolution is of limited potential, justified as it is. It is strictly limited in what it can achieve.

You may say, 'Just a moment! Surely the entire scope of

scientific creationism is not limited to attacking evolution? Does it not provide positive evidences for creation? I find it very difficult to discover any such positive evidence. I doubt whether there will ever be any truly positive proof of creation that is scientific in character. An act of creation represents a discontinuity in natural law and therefore we can never make any comment about it by scientific methodology. It is by definition miraculous, lying outside of the corpus of science. It cannot be addressed in scientific terms. The best we can hope to do with creation science is to demonstrate discontinuity, to show that there must have been some past situation in which natural process was suspended. That does not prove creation, of course, but merely leaves us with creation as a possible explanation of the discontinuity in natural process uncovered by our investigations.

It is, of course, possible to use science to reveal the elegance, wonder and design in the universe, and thence to argue that design and mathematical precision in nature implies an intelligent creator. But that is a philosophical argument, not a scientific one. It is a valid argument, but it is not scientific.

The other great problem is that when we say it is not possible to explain any particular phenomenon (such as the origin of life, for example) in terms of natural law, we are appealing to 'the God of the gaps'. We observe some symbiosis, or some wonder such as the migration of birds, and cannot conceive how an evolutionary account of origins could possibly explain what we observe. But the evolutionist always has the answer that next week, or next year or in a hundred years' time, when science has progressed sufficiently, we shall be able to explain these things by natural law. All we are doing, says the evolutionist, is introducing God when we run out of knowledge. It is very difficult to disagree with that argument as long as we stick to scientific reasoning, however convinced we may be that evolution is wrong and creationism is right.

What about flood geology? Is that not a way of establishing creation as the source of origins? Well, again I think the answer is negative. Whereas the evolutionist attempts to use the fossil record as evidence for evolution, the only thing that we as creationists do with flood geology is to remove the fossil record from the argument. What we say, in fact, is that that this record tells us nothing about origins. It is simply a record of a cataclysmic judgement upon the earth and has no bearing on origins as such. So again we are not making a positive contribution. We are saying, 'Here is a body of evidence that tells us nothing about origins,' and that is an essentially negative statement.

What about all the evidence for a young earth? Is that not positive evidence in favour of a creation model? Again I think the answer is 'no'. For as long as we use young-earth arguments in the absence of any appeal to biblical revelation (and this is the context in which I am speaking at the moment), all we are left with is evidence against the evolutionary time scale. If we establish by scientific study that the earth is young, then all we have done is to deny evolution the time scale that it requires. We have not destroyed evolution, because there could be proposed an alternative evolutionary scenario which provides for a rapid evolution. Such a theory would admittedly be more difficult to maintain but not impossible in principle (cf. punctuated equilibrium). So once again, as long as we keep our creation science divorced from biblical revelation, we are fulfilling a negative role only. We can never establish creation scientifically in the sense that evolutionists *could* establish their theory if it *were* true. For creation lies outside of the scope of natural law, therefore outside of science, whereas evolution if it happened would lie within that scope.

Where does this leave us? Has creation science no value at all? That is not what I am saying. Once we have presented the biblical testimony to creation we may properly turn to a scientific study and demonstrate that observable phenomena are consistent with the biblical creation position. Creation science has an important role, but it is a subsidiary and supportive role to that of biblical creation. It is right for us to use scientific evidence, negatively, to oppose the claims of a particular theory of evolution, and positively to demonstrate that nature is consistent with the biblical revelation. But what I feel we can never do is to establish a satisfactory creation model on the grounds of scientific evidence alone.

The second respect in which scientific creationism fails in its objectives relates to the second of those objectives, namely that if we can persuade someone to accept the creation model as the more reasonable, we shall predispose him to accept the biblical revelation. This is, I fear, a false hope. I have already referred to the fact that many creationists are not Christians, and this is almost sufficient argument by itself to prove my point. An outstanding example is that of the astronomers Hoyle and Wickramasinghe, who have reached a 'creationist' position by scientific argument alone. Life could not possibly have come into being, they say, without the intervention of a superior intelligence. As you read the final chapter of their book *Evolution from space,* a chapter entitled 'Convergence to God', you find that their deity bears no resemblance to the God of the Bible. Deducing creationism from purely intellectual arguments they arrive at a position which is, if anything, further from biblical faith than their starting-point. A person who is convinced of creationism by intellectual or scientific argument is by no means led or predisposed to embrace the Christian teaching on this subject. The reverse may in fact result.

A second danger must now be considered. If creation can be deduced by man's unaided reason, what need is there for revelation? The person who has arrived at a belief without the aid of revelation is less likely to have a high view of revelation. He will either say, 'I have no need of revelation to tell me what I can deduce for myself,' or he will regard the Bible as a human contribution to human knowledge without recognizing Scripture as the Word of God.

Thirdly, this feeling may be reinforced because Scripture actually seems to contradict the position reached. If people have followed the scientific creationist argument, and arrived by intellectual effort at a belief in creation, they could say, 'By scientific study we believe that the worlds were framed by the power of God.' But Scripture (Heb. 11:3) states that it is by faith that we understand these things. By faith we understand that the visible universe was not made from some visible precursor. By faith! Not by intellectual effort. By faith, not by scientific methodology. So our new creationist, who has been persuaded by scientific creationism to adopt a creation model, may say, 'I did not need faith to come to this belief, to arrive at this position. Therefore the Bible contradicts my experience, and if it does so in one place, what credibility can it have elsewhere?'

Fourthly, scientific creationism, if it leads anywhere, leads to deism rather than biblical theism and Christianity. To put it another way, scientific creationism neglects totally the Christology of creationism. Biblical creationism is essentially Christocentric, and this is what I want to demonstrate as I turn to the second part of this discussion.

Biblical creationism; the centrality of Christ

The matters discussed in what follows come closer to the heart of creationism than any of the topics touched upon earlier. Yet strangely they have received scant attention in the current debate on evolution and creation. I refer to the Christology of creation. Our thinking will be based on a passage from chapter 1 of Colossians, beginning in verse 13.

'For [God] delivered us from the domain of darkness, and transferred us to the kingdom of his beloved Son, in whom we have redemption, the forgiveness of sins. And he is the image of the invisible God, the first-born of all creation. For in him all things were created, both in the heavens and on earth, visible and invisible, whether thrones or dominions or rulers or authorities — all things have been created through him and for him. And he is before all things, and in him all things hold together. He is also head of the body, the church; and he is the beginning, the first-born from the dead; so that he himself might come to have first place in everything. For it was the Father's good pleasure for all the fulness to dwell in him, and through him to reconcile all things to himself, having made peace through the blood of his cross; through him, I say, whether things on earth or things in heaven.'

In this passage we see three things in regard to the person of Christ. We see his relationships to God the Father, to the cosmos and to the church. We are going to explore this threefold relationship, for although our point of interest is Christ and the cosmos, it would be a mistake to isolate this one relationship from the others. For Paul quite deliberately links these three things together. He begins with the triune God, moves on to consider Christ and the physical universe and then ends with a dissertation on Christ and the church. These three relationships are, in fact, a unity. Christ's relationship to the created order cannot be understood without reference to his relationship to God and the church. That is the essence of my thesis.

The invisibility of God

Let us begin in verse 15 and consider what we are told here about Christ and God. We read, 'He is the image of the invisible God.'

The first thing we notice is that God is invisible. God cannot be seen, cannot be discerned, cannot be comprehended, by unaided human faculties. The invisibility of God is not a reference solely to the fact that God is spirit, so that we cannot see him with our physical eyes. It speaks, rather, of the unapproachability of God. Of course, these words do include the fact that God is spirit, but they also signify that he is holy. Remember how in Exodus 33:18 Moses makes his great request to God: 'I beseech you, show me your glory.' The reply that he received was definitive of the holiness of God: 'There shall no man see me and live.'

No man can look upon God because he is holy. Even the cherubim in Isaiah's temple vision veiled their eyes in the presence of God. If the sinless angelic beings which serve him ceaselessly must hide their faces, then how much more must we who are both mortal and sinful!

So God is invisible first of all because he is spirit and secondly because he is holy. But there is a third reason why God should be described as 'invisible', namely because he is inscrutable by nature. 'My thoughts are not your thoughts, neither are your ways my ways,' says the Lord (Isa. 55:8). God's thoughts, plans and intentions are beyond our ken. Nobody knows the thoughts in the mind of God. Paul tells us in 1 Corinthians 2:11 that only the Spirit of God can search out the divine mind. It is an enormous privilege that the same Spirit reveals those things, in part, to the believing soul. But this in no way changes the essential truth that the mind of God is inaccessible to human search.

There may be other ways in which the invisibility of God is expressed and demonstrated in Scripture, but what has been said already is enough for us to see the main implication of this teaching. It is clear that if God is to be known to men, *he must declare himself*. This is a most important conclusion and

one that is fundamental to our understanding of the person
and work of Jesus Christ.

Christ, the image of God

It is the uniform teaching of the New Testament that God *has*
declared himself, and has done so in the person of Christ.
Many scriptures substantiate this claim. John begins his
Gospel with a sublime statement of the deity of Christ and
goes on to say, 'No man has seen God at any time; [Christ] the
only-begotten Son, who is in the bosom of the Father, he
has explained him' (John 1:18 mg.). In the sixth chapter,
verse 46, of the same Gospel we read, 'Not that any man has
seen the Father, except the One that is from God, he has seen
the Father.' These and other scriptures are very clear in what
they are saying. God reveals himself through, and only
through, the Son. We might recall the conversation that Jesus
had with his disciple Philip. The latter makes what seems to
be a reasonable request (John 14:8). 'Lord, show us the
Father,' he asks, 'and it is enough for us.' But the response is
anything but predictable: 'Have I been so long with you and
yet you have not come to know me, Philip? He who has seen
me has seen the Father; how do you say, "Show us the
Father"?'

It is therefore in Christ that God makes himself known. It is
in Christ that the invisible God declares and reveals himself.
Notice that it is not a revelation of his *purposes* that he makes
in Christ, but a revelation of *himself*.

Further support for these ideas is to be found in Hebrews
1:3, where we read of Christ, 'He is the radiance of [God's]
glory and the exact representation of his nature.' As the sun's
rays convey to us the light and warmth of the luminary itself,
so God's glory comes to us through Christ. And as the sun
cannot be seen at all except by the reception of those rays, so
God is invisible apart from Christ. Were God knowable
outside of Christ, it would be unnecessary for Christ to be the
exact representation of his nature.

We can turn this around and state the converse. God does
not make himself known except through Christ. He does not
communicate himself to man without Christ. Outside of

Christ there is no true knowledge of God.

I am sure we would all agree that God manifests his saving grace only in Christ, for he alone is the mediator of the new covenant. But the context in Colossians 1 demands a wider interpretation. It extends this idea beyond the question of soteriology. For immediately Paul has told us that Christ is the image of the invisible God, he proceeds to consider Christ in his relationship to the whole cosmos. He does not at this point introduce the subject of salvation, though he comes to it later. Christ is first presented as the image of God in the context, not of salvation, but of creation! There is a great deal in this chapter about the church and the saving work of Christ, but the immediate setting of this statement is the origin and sustenance of the physical universe. The context demands, therefore, that the idea that God reveals himself in Christ be applied to creation as fully as to redemption.

Some objections
God therefore cannot be known truly, regarding all of his work and regarding all of his nature, except in and through Christ. Eliminate Christ and you have an essentially unknown God. I shall put a lot of weight on this conclusion presently and it is only fair therefore that I should pause at this point to consider two possible objections to the claim that I am making.

First of all, it may be argued that God revealed himself in Old Testament revelation, long before Jesus Christ came on the scene of human history. Therefore, surely, he revealed himself without Christ in the Old Testament. Secondly, it might be objected that God stands revealed in the book of nature, that is, through the creation. This seems to be taught in such scriptures as Psalm 19 and Romans 1. Let us look at these objections in turn.

Does the Old Testament constitute a non-Christological revelation of God? My answer to this is negative. We must remember that, as Christians, we must always interpret the Old Testament by the New. We must never think of the two Testaments as distinct, as if they somehow present two different messages. The New Testament will not allow us to treat the Old Testament as a Christless revelation. The Lord Jesus himself emphasized this on the road to Emmaus, when he showed his disciples 'in all the [Old Testament] Scriptures the things concerning himself'. On another occasion, he said of the Law and the Prophets, 'These are they which testify of me.'

Even in relation to the creation story itself, we shall see that the New Testament insists, again and again, that Christ was the Creator. This makes it impossible for us to read the creation story in a way that ignores the role of Christ. We cannot read the Old Testament as if we had not grasped the New. There may in many cases be no explicit references to the Messiah, but as we read the New Testament, the Old is always interpreted for us in Christological terms. Providing we read the Old Testament in the light of the New, the principle that God reveals himself only in Christ remains intact.

The second objection can be voiced in the question: 'Does not God reveal himself outside of Christ in nature?' Obviously we could turn to Romans 1:20,21: 'For since the creation of the world [God's] invisible attributes, his eternal power and divine nature, have been clearly seen, being understood through what has been made, so that they are without excuse. For even though they knew God, they did not honour him as God. . .'

We accept that God's glory, power and Godhead are discernible in nature, but we have to ask two questions. Firstly, is man capable of reading the book of nature? We can easily misunderstand these verses unless we read on to see how ancient man rejected this revelation. Because of sin, man is incapable of correctly reading the book of nature. God is indeed revealed in nature (and in conscience also, as we read in Romans 2:15), and these revelations are such as to leave man without excuse for his atheism. Nevertheless man in his fallen state is incapable of recognizing God in his creation. This avenue of revelation is closed to man because of his fallen nature.

Man cannot say, 'I had no means of knowing about God,' but his blindness to general revelation is both total and culpable. He is dead *in trespasses and sins*. He is dead, being incapable of responding to the stimuli which are there; but he is dead *in sins*. That is, his incapacity is not a misfortune for which he bears no responsibility, but is rather a state for which God holds him fully responsible.

This surely is the import of what Paul writes in Romans 1. The passage starts in 1:18 where we read, 'The wrath of God is revealed from heaven against all ungodliness and unrighteousness of men, who suppress the truth in unrighteousness.' We are left in no doubt that man is guilty for ignoring his Creator. At the same time, man's 'foolish heart was darkened', that is, man is blind to spiritual realities. As Paul writes elsewhere, 'A natural man does not accept the things of the Spirit of God; for they are foolishness to him, and he cannot understand them, because they are spiritually appraised' (1 Cor. 2:14). I do not think Romans 1 is saying that ancient man was once able to perceive God in creation but became progressively blind to him. The sequence recorded by the apostle is surely a logical progression that applies to men of all generations, rather than a historical progression that divides the ancients from ourselves. The logical progression sees unrighteousness as the precursor and cause of spiritual blindness, not the reverse. That is why man remains guilty in his blindness, rather than being an object of pity in the eyes of God.

Although therefore it is true that God is the Author of the book of nature, and although it is true that certain of God's characteristics are revealed in nature, it is still true that man can only know this invisible God through Christ. The book of nature is closed to the eyes of the natural man. He may indeed deduce from nature a belief in a god or gods, but what he sees will bear no resemblance to the true God. I have already cited a modern example of this, namely the views expressed by astronomers Hoyle and Wickramasinghe in their book *Evolution from Space*. They come to the conclusion that life could not have evolved without the intervention of intelligent beings. But they are at pains to point out that these 'gods' are not to be confused with the God of the Bible or indeed the gods of any traditional religion. They remain blind, therefore, to the true being and nature of God, in spite of their 'creationist' insights. It is in Christ, and in Christ alone, that the invisible God effectually reveals himself to man.

If this is the case, if God can be truly known only in Christ, where does this leave our various theories of origins?

Theories of origins
Any theory of origins, whether evolutionary or creationist, that bypasses Christ, must inevitably lead us to false conclusions. That is the thesis that I am advancing in this essay. Whether we are considering atheistical evolution, which obviously leaves Christ out; or theistic evolution, which has a place for God, or at least for a deity, but has no Christological content; or whether we are talking about scientific creationism divorced from Scripture — in all of these cases the theory of origins is bound to be defective since the essential role of Christ is excluded from consideration. (Obviously a Christological content can be superimposed upon theistic evolution and scientific creationism, but it is not of the essence of these theories and is therefore superfluous to them.)

The New Testament places tremendous emphasis upon the fact that Christ is the Creator. Again and again, as we go from John 1 to Colossians 1 to Hebrews 1, we find this insistence that Christ created all things. It is not sufficient in the eyes of the New Testament writers to say that God is the Creator. It has to be Christ. In the prologue to his Gospel, the apostle John goes out of his way to impose a Christology on Genesis 1. He borrows its phraseology: 'In the beginning was the Word.' Compare that with the oft-repeated statement 'God said' in Genesis. He tells us that Christ was 'in the beginning with God' and that 'all things came into being through him'. Just as in Genesis God sent light upon earth, so Christ was 'the true light which. . . enlightens every man' (John 1:1-9).

It seems to me that the New Testament insistence upon a Christocentric creationism is not accidental, an unnecessary gloss on the story of creation. Rather, it is fundamental to the message of the apostles, and there is no clearer demonstration of this fact than the very passage before us in Colossians 1.

Christ and the cosmos
We have considered at some length the relationship of Christ to God. We must now move on, with the apostle, to think of the relationship of Christ to the cosmos. We read, 'He is the first-born of all creation.' This particular statement is sometimes used by unitarians to argue that Christ is part of the created order. He is, they claim, the first-born in the sense of the first created being, through whom God then proceeded

to work out the remainder of the creation. But this is a blatant misinterpretation, and is ruled out of court by the very words that follow at the beginning of verse 16: 'For in him all things were created.' Christ cannot be both the Creator of 'all things' and part of that creation. If he is the Creator of all things, he must necessarily stand outside of the created order.

An even stronger argument to disarm this particular error is to be found in the word 'first-born'. If we turn to the first chapter of Hebrews we find that the distinction is emphasized between Christ, who is 'born', and the angelic orders, who are created. 'To which of the angels did [God] ever say, "Thou art my son, today I have begotten thee"?' (Heb. 1:5.) The argument is that Christ is not created. He is not the work of God's hands but, rather, God's progeny. This is, of course, an anthropomorphism, but the essence of human generation is the fact that the progeny share the nature and characteristics of the parents. This is the whole force of the idea of begetting. He, says John, is the 'only begotten', the one who solely and uniquely shares the attributes of God. Therefore the idea that 'first-begotten' suggests in some way that Christ is part of the creation (albeit the first to be created), is ruled out by the very word itself.

Nor can it be argued that if Christ is the first-begotten, there must have been others, begotten subsequently, who are like him. Therefore he is not unique and cannot be God. For the word 'first-born' may denote pre-eminence rather than chronology. Priority can denote priority in time, the first-born being simply the first child born into a family, or it can signify rank. We can describe the heir to a throne as the first-born in the land even though there are many older than he. The term describes both the blood relationship of the first-born to the sovereign and his rank as the heir to his father's throne. There is therefore no necessary implication that there are others like the first-born. The first child in a family remains the first-born even if it is an only child!

So priority can refer to time or to rank. Fortunately we do not need to debate which is intended in verse 17 because both are found here. Priority in time is, of course, to be understood as priority before time began. 'He is [existed] before all things.' To the Jews who criticized him, Jesus said, 'Before Abraham was, I am.' He took to himself the ineffable and eternal name of God, the 'I AM', the one who stands outside of time, who is the same 'yesterday, today and for ever', as Hebrews tells us of Christ. He is therefore prior in time, the eternal self-existent God, with whom there is neither past nor future, for all is present.

His priority in rank tells us even more about Christ and the cosmos than does his priority in time. First of all, Colossians tells us, he is the Creator. We have already seen that the New Testament always ascribes the work of creation to Christ. 'In him all things were created. . . all things have been created through him and for him' (Col. 1:16).

The biblical writers use several different prepositions in this context. In Hebrews 1, for example, both the Father and the Son are mentioned in relation to creation: 'God. . . has spoken to us in his Son. . . *through* whom also he made the world.' Here in Colossians 1:16 two prepositions are used: '*In* him all things were created' and, at the end of the verse, 'All things have been created *through* him.' The way prepositions are translated often depends on the version consulted. The Authorized Version, for example, says, 'By him were all things created.' I think, however, that the NASV is as close to the original as any in using the words 'in' and 'through'.

What does Paul mean? Does he mean that God the Father created the universe by using Christ as his agent? Is this a reference to the agency of Christ in creation when we read, 'All things were created through him'? I think not. The idea that Christ is the agent of creation is a weaker concept than that which the Bible actually proposes to us. It is a concept that Paul himself had to be careful to avoid in the Colossian context, for one of the problems that Paul had to combat at Colosse was the Gnostic heresy. According to this teaching, Christ was just one of a large succession of spiritual beings, of different ranks and orders, linking the unholy, impure physical world with the remote purity of the spiritual realm. To some extent this is what the Jehovah's Witnesses teach today, that Christ is the great intermediary between God and man but is himself not equal to God.

We have to understand that Paul had consciously to avoid any hint of Gnosticism as he wrote to Colosse. It seems to me therefore that he must be using these two prepositions quite deliberately and with great care.

Although Paul says all things were created 'through Christ', as if speaking of an intermediary or agent, he begins the verse with a different preposition: 'In him all things were created.' This is important. You cannot say of an agent that things were done *in* him. You may say they were done through him, but the word 'in' is not appropriate to an agent. Rather, it implies that the person described is an essential part of the whole picture. We could perhaps paraphrase the meaning thus: 'All things were created in relationship to Christ' or 'with regard to Christ' or 'with reference' to him. We are not to understand the role of Christ as that of an intermediary through whom creation took place, but rather as the creative self-expression of God. That is, the Father's creative will, which brought the entire cosmos into existence, was being expressed in Christ.

Perhaps the easy way to get this across is to say that, just as God was in Christ reconciling the world to himself, so he was in Christ calling that world into being. Christ was not simply an agent through whom God performed this task, but God was in Christ creating the cosmos.

So then we have this priority in rank expressed in the fact that Christ was the Creator. It is of great significance that John calls Christ 'the Word' and links this with the creative activity of God. The expression 'God said. . .' employed in Genesis was not merely a dramatic device or figure of speech. It has special significance in relation to the fact that Christ is the Logos, the Word of God. God's creative acts were brought about by words, the putting forth of the will and mind of God. Words are vehicles of self-expression, and the creation was nothing less than that, an expression of the will of God and, in part, a discovery of his nature. Christ may be the Word of God in other senses, but he is the Word first in this creative sense.

Not only is Christ the Creator, however, but he is the Creator of all. We do not need to spend a great deal of time upon this, but we should notice the emphasis placed upon this claim in verse 16. In fact most of this verse is written to establish the comprehensive character of the creative work of Christ. 'In him all things were created, both in the heavens and on earth, visible and invisible, whether thrones or dominions or rulers or authorities. . . all things have been created through him and for him.'

John places a similar emphasis on the totality of Christ's work, repeating the assertion both positively and negatively: 'All things came into being through him; and apart from him nothing came into being that has come into being' (John 1:3). We might ask why there should be this insistence on the comprehensiveness of the creative work of Christ. Surely it is to combat the Gnostic error in which Christ might be put on the same level as other spiritual dignitaries. If he is the Creator of all, then he stands uniquely above all creation in rank.

This is brought out particularly by the reference to 'thrones, dominions, rulers and authorities'. There is a debate between creationists and theistic evolutionists over the meaning of these terms. The theistic evolutionist does not draw any distinction between creation and providence, since in his view creation was accomplished by providential means rather than by miracle. If by thrones and dominions etc., Paul means the human institutions of history, controlled by the sovereignty of God (Dan. 4:32), then there is no distinction in the verse between Christ creating 'all things' and his providential rule 'over the realm of mankind'.

On the other hand, there is a difference in tense between the act of creation described in verse 16 (they were created) and the sustaining work of providence mentioned in verse 17 ('in him all things *hold* together'). Creation would thus appear to be a finished work lying in the past, while providence remains an ongoing reality. This, of course, is wholly consistent with Genesis 2:1-3, where creation is described as fully complete.

In fact, Paul is almost certainly not speaking of human institutions at all in verse 16. There is no reason for him to pick out these human institutions for special mention. Remember he is seeking to combat a heresy which had erected a whole system of *spiritual* authorities and intermediaries, angelic powers, between God and man, and it is those powers and thrones that Paul here subjects to Christ. Whatever spiritual powers there may be, he says, were created by Christ and therefore cannot be considered superior or even equal to him. Paul does not deny the existence of spiritual powers. He refers to them on various occasions, notably in Ephesians 3:10 and 6:12 ('rulers and the authorities in the heavenly places'). But what he does insist is that Christ is always superior to them (Hebrews 1:4).

It seems to me that the apostle is simply using human analogies and terms of sovereignty and rule to describe the angelic powers with which alone he is concerned in this part of the epistle (see e.g. 1:13, 2:8-10, 2:15-18).

So Christ is the Creator of all things, but that is not all. His priority is further demonstrated by the fact that he is the sustainer of the cosmos ('In him all things consist,' v. 17). That is to say, all things derive their integrity from the very existence and will of Christ. The same truth is taught in Hebrews 1:3 where we read that he 'upholds all things by the word of his power'.

It is here that we see the link between the Christology of the New Testament and the nature of science. When Hebrews tells us that Christ sustains the universe by the word of his power, it can be understood, in part at least, as a reference to the laws of nature. In scientific terms the universe is 'upheld' by the operation of natural law. It is this which imposes integrity and continuity upon the physical cosmos and it is this, we are told, that is achieved continually by the word of Christ's power. In one sense, therefore, the laws of science are God's powerful word, the moment-by-moment expression of his divine will.

A final and most important point arises in our discussion of Christ's priority in rank. We are told in verse 16 that all things were created *for* him. It seems to me that here we have a clear statement of the very purpose of the cosmos. All things were created not only in Christ, not only through Christ, but also for him. That is to say, it is the intention of God that the cosmos should subserve the glory and fulfilment of Christ. The cosmos can be seen as an arena in which the glory of Christ is demonstrated, in which the purposes of Christ are worked out, and in which the will, mind and character of Christ can be expressed. That, according to the apostle, is the purpose of the cosmos.

This is a most important idea. We usually think of the cosmos as just being 'there', as if it were simply part of a deistic scheme of things. Then, quite separately, we think of Jesus Christ coming to earth for the purpose of saving sinners. The latter, of course, is perfectly correct, but the New Testament does not present things in quite this way. There are few chapters of the Bible that say as much about the saving work of Christ as does Colossians 1. Read verses 13,14 and 20-23. But it is this very subject of salvation that leads Paul to introduce the cosmic role of Christ. He sees the cross of Christ as the place where God was reconciling not only sinners but *all things* to himself (v. 20), whether on earth or in heaven. If the work of Christ is to carry this wider significance, then Christ himself must be seen as the Creator and Sustainer of the cosmos. No smaller view of him is admissible if he is to be the Reconciler of all things. No lesser view properly represents the saving work of Christ in all its fulness and cosmic implication.

Christ and the church
We now turn to our final topic, the relationship of Christ to the church. Clearly we could examine this relationship at great length, exploring it in many ways, in many figures and in many great doctrines. That, however, is not my purpose here. What I want to point out is the way his relationship to the church is linked with his relationship to the cosmos. Looking at our passage, you see there is no real pause between verses 17 and 18. 'He is before all things, and in him all things hold together. He is also head of the body, the church.' There is no change of 'gear' at this point. The argument flows smoothly from one verse to the next. Paul's theme is the pre-eminence of Christ in *all* realms, whether church, cosmos or heaven.

If we look back to Ephesians 1:22-23 we find an even more striking example of the way Paul relates Christ's cosmic role to his headship of the church. It is a brief statement that can easily be missed. We read, '[God has] put all things in subjection under his feet, and gave him as head over all things to the church, which is his body, the fulness of him who fills all in all.' Notice that he is not just head over all things (the cosmic Christ). Nor is he simply head over the church (the Saviour), but head over all things *to* the church.

What does that mean? Let us express it in this way. Christ is head over all things *for the sake of the church*. His dominance and priority over the created order is for the sake or benefit of the church. Of course, the converse is true, that the church exists for the sake and glory of Christ, since we have already seen that the whole of creation is 'for' him. But it is equally true that creation is not just for the benefit of Christ in a vague and general sense. Creation is for Christ *through* the church, and this leads us to the sobering thought that the church of Jesus Christ is really the *raison d'être* of creation. The cosmos exists in order that the church might exist!

In case this seems to be a rather extreme statement, let us consider further what Paul is saying in Ephesians 1:23: 'The church, which is his body, [is] the fulness of him who fills all in all.' Now that is a staggering claim. The church (that is, the glorified church) is the fulness of Christ. Christ is fulfilled in the church.

How can this be? How can any created entity fulfil Christ? How can God become in any way more complete or perfect? At first sight the idea seems inadmissible, for it implies that the perfection of God is somehow incomplete without the church. Surely he is perfect to begin with? Yet the New Testament teaches clearly that, somehow, Christ *is* fulfilled in the church, for the church is the fulness of him who fills all in all.

Perhaps we can glimpse an understanding of what all this means by using another great New Testament picture of the church, namely that it is the bride of Christ. If marriage can be regarded as the consummation of manhood and womanhood, then by analogy we can see how Christ's union with the church can be described as his 'fulness'. The uniting of human partners fulfils certain potentialities, certain possibilities which are present but dormant until the marriage is established and consummated. Thus we can see how the church may be the fulness of Christ since it fulfils his potential for love, grace, mercy and saving power, characteristics of the Godhead that would remain for ever unexpressed without the church.

Here, then, we have the element that completes Paul's unifying picture of Christ and the cosmos. The universe was created for Christ, not only in a general sense, but specifically that the church might come into being. As the bride of Christ, that glorified church represents the culmination of God's ultimate purpose, 'the summing up of all things in Christ' (Eph. 1:10).

Conclusion

There are, of course, many other passages of Scripture, verses full of significance for the matters we have been studying, which we have not space to discuss. There is even much in Colossians 1 that we have not considered and which would illuminate the subject of Christ and the cosmos. What has been said, however, should help us to see how important it is to have a Christological view of creation. Mere creationism, or even scientific creationism, can never be enough. Nor is it sufficient that such creationism is held and promoted by Bible-believing Christians. We must insist that a right emphasis be placed on the Christology of creation.

Reference

1. Newton, Isaac.
   Letter dated 10 Dec. 1692, in 'Four letters from Sir Isaac Newton to Doctor Bentley containing some arguments in Proof of a Deity' (1756) p.1.

3.

The genealogies in Scripture

David T. Rosevear

The theory of evolution depends for its acceptance upon long periods of time having passed from the emergence of the first life on earth to the appearance of man. Even allowing billions of years, many would find evolution implausible, but given only some six thousand years all would agree that evolution would be impossible. Creationists claim that there is good scientific evidence for a young earth. The Bible provides historical evidence for a recent creation. This is based on the authenticity and completeness of the genealogies which link Adam and Noah with historical figures such as Abraham and David. Evolutionists must dismiss the early chapters of Genesis as myth. Adam expelled from the Garden of Eden, Noah's catastrophic flood and the Tower of Babel were designed to teach certain truths, we are told. They may have been based on local incidents but have become exaggerated by repetition. They are similar to the story of Icarus, who flew too close to the sun — according to evolutionists. This paper looks at the genealogies of Scripture, considers their implications and discusses some of the difficulties.

It is said of the sons of Simeon in 1 Chronicles 4:33 that they kept a genealogical record. Proving family connections was necessary in controversies over the ownership of land (Ruth 4:4). We read in Nehemiah 7 that those priests returning from the upheaval of the Exile who could not find their family records were excluded from the priesthood. The royal line particularly would be recorded because of the hope of the coming of Messiah, but every Jew was proud to be able to trace his ancestry back to father Abraham. The command to avoid controversies over genealogies (1 Tim. 1:4; Titus 3:9) is obscure but cannot refer to the lists found in the Bible, since the same writer also tells us that all Scripture is useful for teaching (2 Tim. 3:16). Genealogies are pertinent in the Old Testament, where God is preserving the integrity of a people peculiar to himself. In the fulness of time, God sent his Son, born of a woman and under the law, to complete the revelation of himself. Consequently, genealogies are not found in the New Testament, with the exception of those of Jesus Christ himself. Genealogies indicate sonship and inheritance, and in this age of grace all may become the sons of God (John 1:12) having an inheritance that can never perish, spoil or fade (1 Peter 1:4). Genealogies are about kings, priests and God's people, and now all may belong to a chosen people, a royal priesthood, a holy nation, God's peculiar people (1 Peter 2:9). And all may draw near to God through a High Priest who in one sense is without genealogy, without beginning of days or end of life (Heb. 7:3).

The dating of events in the history of the Jews is carefully recorded, in contrast to those of other ancient peoples. Manetho's lists of Egyptian kings was written as late as 250 B.C., and is only preserved in a few inaccurate quotations in other writings. However, in Scripture we have such statements as: 'The time that the people of Israel lived in Egypt was 430 years' (Exod. 12:40). 'In the 480th year after the people of Israel came out of Egypt, in the fourth year of Solomon's reign over Israel, in the month of Ziv, which is the second month, he began to build the house of the Lord' (1 Kings 6:1). 'In the first year of Cyrus, king of Persia. . .' (Ezra 1:1). 'In the fifteenth year of the reign of Tiberius Caesar. . .' (Luke 3:1).

Genealogies in the Scriptures can be broadly classified into two types. Some are merely lists of names in sequence, not always complete. For example, if we compare Ezra's family tree back to Aaron in Ezra 7 with the analogous list in 1 Chronicles 6, we find an extra six names in the latter. Since the writers are concerned to show descent and inheritance, completeness was not essential to their task. The longer list of

the Chronicler fits the time span better. However, the list
from Abraham to Solomon in 1 Chronicles 2 would seem too
short to cover about a thousand years. There would appear to
be eleven generations from Joseph to Joshua but only four
from Judah to Achan and four also from Levi to Eleazar.
Evidently there are omissions in the last two, since they all
cover about four hundred years (see Fig. 1).

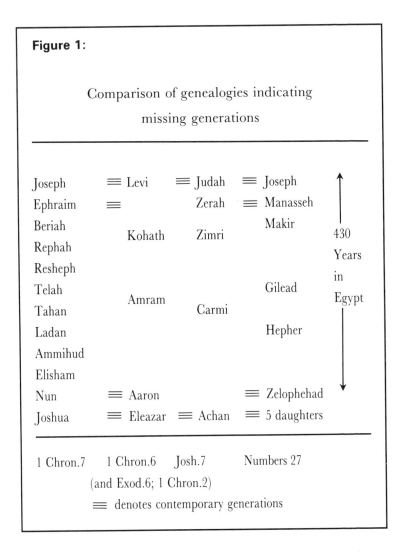

Figure 1:

Comparison of genealogies indicating

missing generations

Joseph	≡ Levi	≡ Judah	≡ Joseph	
Ephraim	≡		Zerah	≡ Manasseh	
Beriah		Kohath	Zimri	Makir	430
Rephah					Years
Resheph					in
Telah		Amram		Gilead	Egypt
Tahan			Carmi		
Ladan				Hepher	
Ammihud					
Elisham					
Nun	≡ Aaron		≡ Zelophehad	
Joshua	≡ Eleazar	≡ Achan	≡ 5 daughters	

1 Chron.7   1 Chron.6   Josh.7   Numbers 27
             (and Exod.6; 1 Chron.2)
                ≡ denotes contemporary generations

The second type of genealogy adds sufficient detail to show that the lists are complete and to indicate the passage of time. Examples of these are the genealogies of the kings of Judah and Israel which are interspersed in the narrative matter in Kings and Chronicles: e.g., 'In the eighteenth year of Jehoshaphat king of Judah, Jehoram the son of Ahab became king over Israel in Samaria, and he reigned for twelve years' (2 Kings 3:1). With this type of genealogy we can sum the individual reigns to find the number of years from, say, Solomon's ascension till the Exile (see Fig. 2).

There are two family trees of Jesus Christ. One in Luke's Gospel chapter 3 traces the ancestry back through David and Abraham to Adam 'the son of God'. The other in Matthew chapter 1 gives the descent from Abraham through David. Luke's line from Abraham back to Adam agrees with the genealogies found in Genesis chapters 5 and 11, and would have been copied from that source. Matthew's and Luke's line between Abraham and David agree together and with genealogies found in 1 Chronicles chapters 1 and 2. (1 Chronicles 1 also repeats the line from Adam to Abraham.) However, from David to Jesus Christ the two Gospels differ completely. Matthew's is the royal line of descent whereby Christ inherits the throne of his 'father' David, and the term 'begat' signifies heritage as well as sonship. For example, 'Salathiel begat Zorobabel,' but 1 Chronicles chapter 3 tells us that Zerubbabel was the nephew of Shealtiel (Salathiel). Under Jewish law, as our own, a nephew would inherit where a man died without issue. Matthew's Messiah inherits the throne of David through 'Joseph, the husband of Mary, of whom was born Jesus, who is called Christ'. 'Of whom' is the feminine singular, contending that Joseph had no part in this birth. A comparison of the names reveals that, though Matthew almost certainly took his material from 1 Chronicles, he deliberately left out four generations in order to give patterns of fourteen steps. Since Luke's line is much longer than Matthew's between David and Christ, it is probable that Matthew omitted more generations still. This is permissible since 'begat' implies a line of descent, succession or birthright rather than a father to son relationship.

Luke is concerned with the humanity of Jesus and so traces the Lord's family tree from his mother Mary back through

David's son Nathan and then right back to Adam. Zorababel and Salathiel are names which feature in this list too, but do not refer to the princes of those names in Matthew's line. Other common names occur more than once in Luke's genealogy, such as Matthat, Joseph and Levi, as one would expect.

Turning to the genealogies of Genesis chapters 5 and 11, can we say, as many who hold to the creation model have said, that the term 'begat' implies only descent, and that, as with Matthew's line, some generations have been left out? This

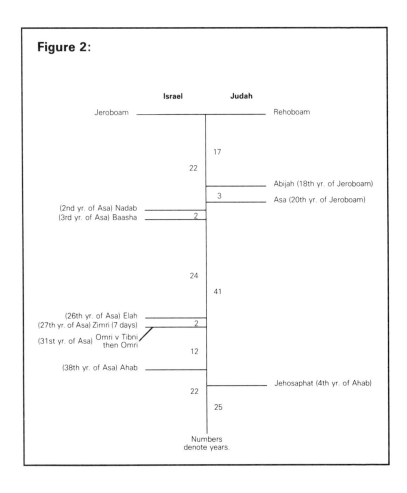

Figure 2:

Israel   Judah

Jeroboam ———————————————— Rehoboam

17

22

Abijah (18th yr. of Jeroboam)

3   Asa (20th yr. of Jeroboam)

(2nd yr. of Asa) Nadab ——————————
(3rd yr. of Asa) Baasha —————————— 2

24

41

(26th yr. of Asa) Elah ———————————
(27th yr. of Asa) Zimri (7 days)   2

(31st yr. of Asa) Omri v Tibni then Omri

12

(38th yr. of Asa) Ahab ——————————

Jehosaphat (4th yr. of Ahab)

22

25

Numbers denote years.

would push back the time since the creation of man from
about 4,000 B.C. to an indeterminate age more in line with
current scientific thought. Jude, in his short letter at the other
end of the Bible, evidently considered the term 'begat' to
denote a father-son relationship here, for he refers to Enoch as
the seventh from Adam. Further, we are given details in these
genealogies, rather as with the kings of Israel and Judah,
which allow one to build up a time scale and which preclude
the possibility of missing generations. For example, we read
that when Adam was 130 years old, he fathered Seth, that
Adam lived a further 800 years after fathering Seth, having
other sons and daughters, and that he lived a total of 930 years
and then died. There is no room for ambiguity here, and we
can build up a chart (Fig. 3) which enables us to add the
years together, just as Ussher did, to arrive at 4,004 B.C.
What is more, Genesis 4 gives the line of Cain with the same
number of generations to the Flood, suggesting that both are
complete. In Luke 3:36, however, we find the name Cainan,
which does not occur in 1 Chronicles 1. The Septuagint
version in both Genesis 10:24 and 11:12 includes Cainan,
adding a further 130 years to the tally. As Niessen has pointed
out[1], not only has the Septuagint version acquired Cainan
(Cain sounds like the Hebrew for acquired — Gen. 4:1) but
it has also added many years to the ages in the two
genealogies, so that Methuselah is made to survive the Flood!
The Septuagint was published in Egypt shortly after Manetho's Egyptian chronology and it could be that these scribes
were pressurized to bring their time scale into line with that of
Manetho. Many of the church fathers regarded Cainan as
superfluous. However, if Cainan is genuine, this allows an
expansion of the time scale, with other possible omissions.[2]
Seaver has shown by a statistical analysis of these genealogies
that there was an approximately exponential decay in life
spans from the Flood to Moses' time.[3] This fits in with the
general observation that displaced systems normally regain
equilibrium by an asymptotic exponential curve. The inclusion of Cainan throws the curve off the predicted line. To fit
the expected curve, any omissions would have to be systematically spaced rather than random, which is highly improbable.
When the longer Septuagint ages are plotted they give a linear
decay, contrary to expectation.

Figure 3:

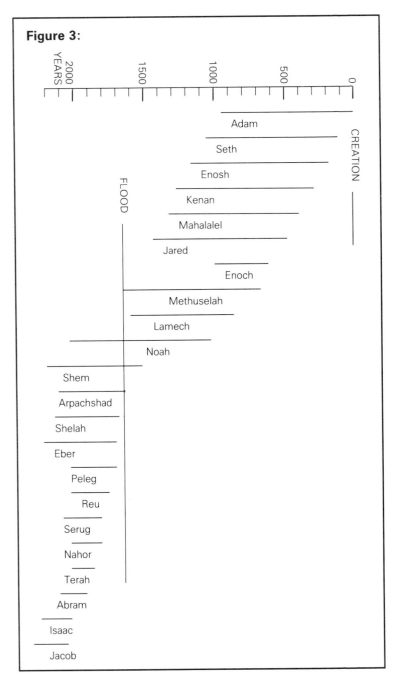

An immediate problem is the longevity of the antediluvians. Some have suggested that the time period was not a year but a moon, so that by dividing by thirteen, Methuselah's 969 years become an unexceptional 74. However, by such accounting, Enoch was only $65 \div 13$ or 5 when he fathered Methuselah, which is somewhat precocious! With the exception of this Enoch, whom God took early, all before the Flood lived about nine hundred years, but most of those born after the Flood lived a mere one hundred and twenty or so years. Many later generations died before their ancestors; for instance Shem outlived Abraham. This was a sudden change, remarked in Genesis 6:3. Shem was still alive in Jacob's time and Jacob could say to Pharaoh, "I'm a hundred and thirty years old. Few have been my years, unlike my fathers' " (Gen. 47:9). If there was a sudden shortening of the life-span after the Flood we must look for the reason in the changed conditions. The ageing process is not yet understood. The self-replicating mechanism of DNA in cell nuclei seems designed to prevent change and decay. Perhaps ageing is brought about by mutations in the DNA caused by radiation. Did radiation levels change after the Flood? Genesis 1:7 refers to waters above the firmament and waters under the firmament, generally interpreted as meaning a layer of water vapour above the atmosphere. Chapter 2:5 says there was no rain, but a mist watered the ground, so presumably the rivers were derived from springs, as with Ezekiel 47 and Revelation 22. Immediately after the Flood, in which the water vapour was precipitated and the fountains of the great deep were broken up, we get the first mention of wind. It has been pointed out that after the formation of the earth, which even today is still hot inside, one would expect a deep layer of water vapour above the atmosphere, providing a shield from cosmic radiation. The removal of this shield with the Flood would lead to an increased level of radiation, possibly causing mutations of genes leading to hereditary diseases and maybe accelerating ageing. Such effects would show themselves abruptly after the Flood. So we have a feasible explanation for the great age of early man, as recorded in the Bible and encountered in the folklore of many peoples.

If man had been around for even 500,000 years, it is estimated that the world population today should be more than three hundred times its present figure of 3×10^9. In fact, population figures support an age for man of 5,000 to 10,000 years. Is it coincidence that written records on stone and baked clay, all the trappings of civilization, fine enamelling, metal work and civil engineering works, all go back less than 6,000 years? Is it coincidence that in the folklore of ancient peoples, often in a corrupt form, there are tales of long-lived ancestors and a flood? Is it not stretching credulity to imagine that intelligent man spent millions of years as a cave man, with zero population growth, and that then 5,000 years ago suddenly he became civilized and began to multiply upon the face of the earth?

It is often claimed that the early chapters of Genesis are folklore, passed down from one generation to another around the camp fires and becoming embellished with the telling. However we see from these genealogies (Fig. 3) that one man, Methuselah, could have known every member of this family tree from Adam to Shem over hundreds of years of active life. This gives to the whole record the validity of a first-hand account. Again, after the Flood, Noah and Shem were contemporary with Abraham. The writer to the Hebrews tells us that by faith, Abraham, when he was called to go out into a place which he would later receive as an inheritance, obeyed; and went out, not knowing where he was going (Heb. 11:8). How much more probable that this was not blind faith, but faith based upon experience of a faithful God and the testimony of men like Noah and Shem!

The great-grandson of Shem was Eber, born only sixty-seven years after the Flood. He outlived six succeeding generations. He is now known to archaeologists from inscriptions showing him to have been a leader of the people. Genesis 10:21 refers to Shem as the father of all the children of Eber, and from his name the word 'Hebrews' is derived. Eber called his son Peleg, which means 'divided', for in his days the earth was divided (Gen. 10:25). Population estimates indicate that from eight persons after the Flood the family would just be reaching the point where it was not possible to know everyone. So to keep their identity they built a tower, probably similar to the Ziggurat at Ur.

Archaeology, history, folklore and statistics all suggest that the genealogies are an accurate and complete account of the early history of mankind. This gives a date for the creation of about 4,000 B.C. Prophecies concerning the second coming of the Lord Jesus Christ strongly suggest that we, at the close of the sixth millennium, live in the last days. The psalmist and Peter speak of 1,000 years being as a day with the Lord. Perhaps it is not too fanciful to relate the six days of creation to the past six thousand years and the coming millennium to God's sabbath rest. The night is far spent, the day is at hand: let us therefore cast off the works of darkness and let us put on the armour of light. We are God's peculiar people, that we should show forth the praises of him who has called us out of darkness into his marvellous light. In the time past we were not a people, but are now the people of God.

References

1. Richard Niessen, *Creation Research Society Quarterly*, *19*, (1982), 60.
2. Henry M. Morris and John C. Whitcomb, *The Genesis Flood*, (Presbyterian and Reformed, Philadelphia, 1961), Appendix II.
3. William Seaver, *C.R.S.Q.*, *20*, (1983), 80.

Part II

Evolution and Man

4.

Evolution and the humanities

Willem J. Ouweneel

There are many people, particularly people with an education other than in the natural sciences, who live with a false presupposition. They think that evolutionary problems are of interest to biologists and geologists, but have little to do with their own fields of research and even less with everyday life. This is a dangerous misapprehension. There is not a single field of research, and therefore not a single aspect of modern life, that has not been influenced by evolutionism to a greater or lesser extent. This had been predicted by Darwin himself. Near the end of *The Origin of Species,* after having described the impact that his theory would have on the natural sciences, he wrote, 'In the future I see an open field for far more important researches. Psychology will be securely based on the foundation. . . of the necessary acquirement of each mental power and capacity by gradation. Much light will be thrown on the origin of man and his history.'[1] It is on psychology that I myself will speak in particular; however, not only psychology but all the humanities have been strongly modified by the doctrine of evolution. Bewkes *et al.* wrote in 1940 that this doctrine provided a new approach in astronomy, geology, philosophy, ethics, religion and the history of social institutions.[2]

The cause of this tremendous effect can easily be pointed out. The concept of evolution led many natural scientists to assume a totally different world-view (*Weltanschauung*), a naturalistic world-view in which creation was replaced by evolution and in which there was no place for supernatural reality or miracles. However, if the world-view of the scientist was totally changed, this could not be without an effect upon the view of man (*Menschanschauung*) in the field of the humanities. The 'humanities' involve the study of that most remarkable of all creatures, man. Psychology in particular makes the pretension of being the science that empirically investigates the essence of man. Since the beginning of empirical psychology — a little over a hundred years ago — many have thought it possible to explore the deepest essence of man simply by observations and experiments. Such people saw science as a 'neutral, objective, unbiased' enterprise, a human activity that could be carried out without any religious or philosophical prejudice.

Prejudiced psychology

Today we know better. There are no human activities at all which are entirely 'neutral and objective', and this includes scientific research. Psychology itself has provided evidence that *all* our observations are 'coloured' or prejudiced. Our sensory impressions are carried from our senses to the cerebral trunk, from where they are transported to the cerebral cortex, where they are brought to consciousness. But on their way from the trunk to the cortex they have to pass the lobes of the so-called limbic brain system. Here they are 'charged' with the huge arsenal of experiences, learned reflexes and emotions, attitudes, ideas, habits, tendencies (constitutional or learned) of which we are scarcely conscious but which impart a certain (sensitive) 'colour' to all our observations.[3] This happens continuously, also, in scientific activity. And where would this be more true than in those sciences which are occupied with 'ourselves', whose subject is man himself? Every psychologist who starts an investigation begins *a priori* with certain presupposed (partly unconscious) ideas about who and what man actually 'is'. Those ideas determine the choice of his experiments and affect the interpretation of their results.

Christians who set out to study one of the humanities today

are confronted with the problem that the scholars who developed the humanities were not Christians. If we were discussing mechanical engineering or dental surgery this would not be so bad; but we have to do here with sciences that have pretended, from the beginning, to tell us something essential about who and what man 'is'. Today the humanities are more modest as to this point than they were, but the idea is still prevalent.

Now, the founders and early representatives of the humanities *all* had this in common: they held the view that man was no longer a person created in the image of God, but an elevated animal governed by drives and instincts. All that is essential in man was reduced, not to his relation to the Creator, but to his presumed origins from the animal kingdom. The psychologist C.H. Judd expressed it thus: 'If. . . psychology is to gain a complete understanding of human nature, it must take into account the findings of the science of biology, which traces man's bodily structures and some of his traits back to remote origins in the lower forms of animal life.'[4] It is obvious that whatever such psychologists discover about man, although interesting, can only be 'half truths', at best, because they start from a totally wrong view of man, as we shall presently see.

This is the reason that the Christian who wants to study the humanities cannot just pray for God's keeping care and assume a critical attitude towards his field of study. He needs a radically *Christian* psychology, built up anew from the very foundation. Such a Christian psychology starts from the revealed Word of God, the Bible, which gives us not only the full truth about God but also about man, about ourselves. This is precisely the truth that can never be *acquired* in an experimental way but can only be *received* by way of divine revelation. Here only, the true essence of man (or to put it biblically, the *heart* of man) is brought to light. Only in the light of the divine revelation about man is a true, empirical study of the humanities possible. It is not enough to point out the influence of evolutionism within the humanities and to fight against it. If we had merely done this in biology and geology, we would not be far today. Our strength has always been, not only to refute evolutionism, but to set over against the evolution model a positive creation model. In precisely the same way we badly need a positive creation model in the humanities. I have recently tried to develop such a model in human psychology.[5] This model is very complicated, so that I have to limit myself to some of its principal features.

Christian model of man

At the beginning of creation, and on the third, the fifth and the sixth days of creation, five kingdoms were created which could be described as follows:
1. The *physical* (or *inorganic*) kingdom, i.e. the material, lifeless created things;
2. the *biotic* (or *organic,* or *vegetative*) kingdom, i.e. plants: living organisms without perception and feeling;
3. the *perceptive* kingdom, i.e. lower animals, which have perceptions (sensory awareness) through the possession of senses and a nervous system, and have instincts and reflexes based on such perceptions, but have no differentiated feelings;
4. the *sensitive* kingdom, i.e. mammals, which do not only have organic and perceptive life but also a differentiated life of feeling (affections, emotions) particularly due to their limbic brain lobes lacking in lower animals;
5. the *spiritive*[6] kingdom, i.e. the world of man, who knows not only organic, perceptive and sensitive life but also a richly differentiated life of thought, imagination and volition.

When we consider these five kingdoms we soon discover that each of the four higher ones encloses the previous one(s). Man, for example, is a typically 'spiritive' being, but he also exhibits sensitive, perceptive, biotic and physical *aspects,* although the spiritive aspect is the characteristic one. Similarly, mammals are characteristically sensitive beings, but they also have perceptive, biotic and physical aspects. This implies that, across our division into kingdoms, we can make a division into aspects ('aspects' are viewpoints from which we can consider things or organisms, see figure opposite). Every 'higher' aspect presupposes the 'lower' aspects, which means that, for example, in our world we do not know perceptive beings that are not at the same time

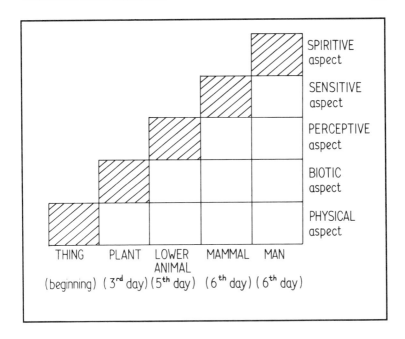

biotic and physical beings, but we do know perceptive beings that are not sensitive or spiritive beings.

In the past, many scholars have tried to reduce or trace these various aspects *to one another,* and have thereby over-looked the fact that *the Creator* has ordained these various aspects, or modes of being, in the cosmos. All aspects, all modes of being, should be 'reduced' to their Creator, *not* to one of those aspects themselves, which thereby would be deified and idolized. Thus, materialists do not deny the sensitive or the spiritive, but maintain that ultimately these are nothing but special forms of the physical. Spiritualists have asserted the opposite, that is, they maintain that eventually all is spiritual (or spiritive). Interestingly, since the last century, both materialists and spiritualists have tried to 'prove' their position by means of the evolutionary doctrine. Materialists say, '*Because* the spiritual has evolved from the physical it can be nothing else than some special form of the physical.' Spiritualists (like many occultists today) say, '*Because* the spiritual has evolved from the physical the spiritual must already have been present within the physical

in some encapsulated way. In plants, the spiritual is partially
unfurled into organic life.' In animals, it is further developed
into perceptive and sensitive life. So they argue. Of course,
materialistic and spiritualistic evolutionists differ very much,
but in one point they agree: they seek the ground of all things
within visible reality itself, within the created cosmos. In the
Christian view, by contrast, we seek this ground *outside*
creation, i.e. in God. He is the Creator and the Preserver of all
things. All the various aspects of the cosmos find their
unbreakable unity in him, who rules them by his laws and
ordinances.

In our model of man we must now make a big step forward.
We will distinguish not only five aspects but also five different
structures in man. By these we mean five different organizational levels in man, each governed by its own laws,
instituted by the Creator. The important point about these
five structures is that each one of them *functions in all five
aspects,* but is characterized by only one aspect in particular.
Let us look briefly at these five structures by first comparing
them with the *two* structures we postulate for a plant:

   1. The *physical* structure, comprising the chemical consti-
      tuents, physical processes and chemical reactions. This
      structure exhibits *two* aspects:

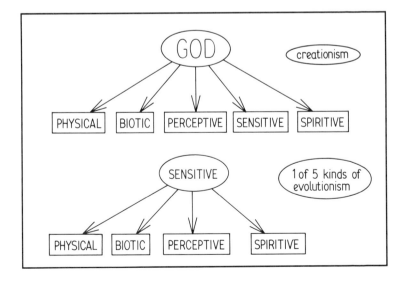

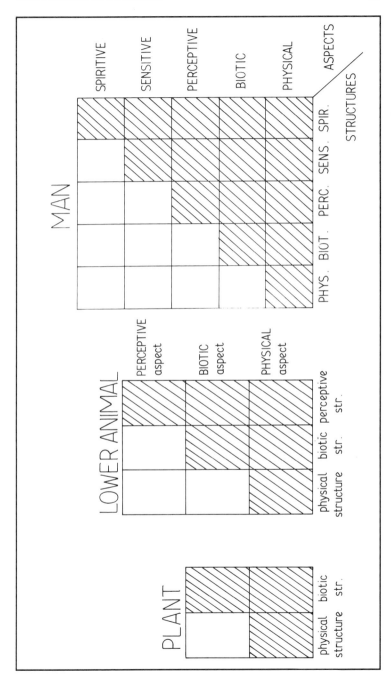

    a. the *physical* aspect: plant-matter is subject to physico-chemical laws;

    b. the *biotic* aspect: plant-matter as such is not subject to biotic laws, but on the other hand it greatly differs from the matter of, for example, a stone: plant-matter is, and stone-matter is not, made up in such a way that it can 'carry', or make possible, organic life. (A stone therefore exhibits one structure only, the physical structure, and is subject to the laws of one aspect only — the physical aspect.)

  2. The *biotic* structure, comprising the cell, tissue and organ structure and the physiological life processes. Here again we distinguish the same *two* aspects:

    a. the *physical* aspect: life processes in the plant have their own, biotic laws, which differ from physical laws, but they are, on the other hand, *'carried'* by physico-chemical structures and processes;

    b. the *biotic* aspect: life processes are subject to biotic laws, and therefore we say that this second structure is *characterized* by this second aspect, so that we call it the biotic structure.

Note that the higher structure comprises or encapsulates, the lower one.

The mental structures

In the same way, we distinguish in a lower animal like the fly a hierarchic encapsulation of *three* structures. Both the physical and the biotic structures of the fly differ essentially from those of the plant because in the former they anticipate the possibility of sensory perception, that is, the simplest form of consciousness, and in the latter they do not. Therefore, we distinguish in these structures in the fly not two but three aspects, including the perceptive aspect. Specifically: physical fly-matter and biotic fly-organs ('brains') exhibit physical and biotic processes which 'carry' the perceptive processes characteristic of the *third,* the *perceptive* structure, which functions in the physical, the biotic and the perceptive aspect. In the same way, it can easily be seen that a mouse exhibits *four* structures, each functioning in *four* different aspects, so that the physical, the biotic and the perceptive structure of a mouse are essentially different from those of a fly because they

can 'carry' sensitive (affective, emotive) processes, characteristic of the fourth, the *sensitive* structure. We remember two
things:

1. Higher organisms are not simply lower organisms plus
   something new; they are essentially different. The material substance, the life processes, the perceptions and
   the feelings of man are in some way similar to those in
   lower organisms, but in other respects they are essentially
   different: they are uniquely constructed in such a way that
   they can 'carry' the whole of the spiritive life of man, in
   contrast to those of the mouse.

2. The newer aspects of higher organisms can never be
   reduced to the aspects of lower organisms: the spiritive
   cannot be reduced to the sensitive, the perceptive, the
   biotic or the physical.

Particularly in the human brain, we clearly see that human
matter, life processes, perceptions and feelings are uniquely
constituted in such a way as to make possible unique human
phenomena such as thinking, imagination, volition — typically spiritive phenomena.

Let us look at the three highest, or *mental*, structures a little
more closely.

1. The *perceptive* structure, comprising perception (sensory
   awareness) and some phenomena directly based on it,
   such as:

   a. *instincts;* an instinct is an innate, irreflective behavi-
      oural response to a given stimulus, typical and useful
      for the species concerned; in man perhaps only the
      suckling instinct;

   b. *reflexes;* a reflex is an immediate, involuntary response
      to a given stimulus not involving the brain, but
      involving perception (like the flight reflex, which we
      distinguish from a purely physiological reflex like the
      eye pupil reflex); reflexes are innate or learned (by a
      process called conditioning);

   c. *tendencies;* I call an inward awareness of a given
      physiological need a 'tendency'; for example, the body
      needs food, and this need of food we experience as
      'appetite'.

   In man this structure is particularly 'carried' by the
   cerebral truck, but the cerebellum also plays a role.

2. The *sensitive* structure, comprising the inward feelings:
   a. *affections:* being attracted or repelled by; the capacity to find something (not) pleasant, beautiful, nice, lovely;
   b. *impulses:* inclinations, desires, lusts, cravings; often called 'drives'; they differ from tendencies by their sensitive 'plus';
   c. *emotions:* inward movements, (suddenly) being 'touched' by joy, love-sickness, *or* grief, anger, fear.

   In man, this structure is particularly 'carried' by the limbic brain lobes.

3. The *spiritive* structure, comprising spiritive life:
   a. *cognition:* (getting to) know something through thought, argument, deliberation;
   b. *imagination:* both in the sense of fancy, realizing, visualizing, and of creative devising, contriving;
   c. *volition:* striving for, desiring, choosing, deciding, in a conscious, reflective way.

   This structure, unique for man and irreducible to lower structures, is particularly 'carried' by the cerebral cortex of the brain-hemispheres, which are well developed in man only.

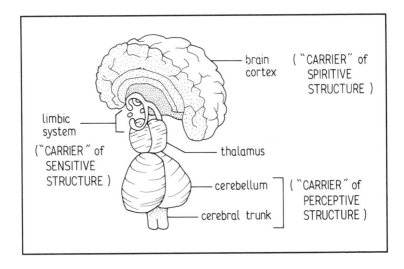

Spiritive life in man is so richly developed that it can be considered from more than one point of view. Thus we find that cognitive, imaginative or volitional 'acts' (inward spiritive activities) can be typically *analytical* (like the acts of a scientist), *cultural-historical* (like those of a technician or politician), *lingual* (when looking for words to express our thoughts), *social* (acts characterized by interhuman contact, communion), *economic* (administrative, saving, evaluating acts), *aesthetic* (acts characterized by standards of harmony and beauty), *juridical* (standards of right and righteousness), *ethical* (standards of benevolence, love) and *pistical* (standards of faith, persuasion). A third point of view is the consideration that acts are determined by *constitutional* factors (mainly depending on hereditary factors, but also on the physical and mental condition of the moment), *learning* factors (all perceptive reflexes, sensitive responses and spiritive skills that we learn from infancy onward), and *motivational* factors (perceptive tendencies, sensitive impulses and spiritive volition).

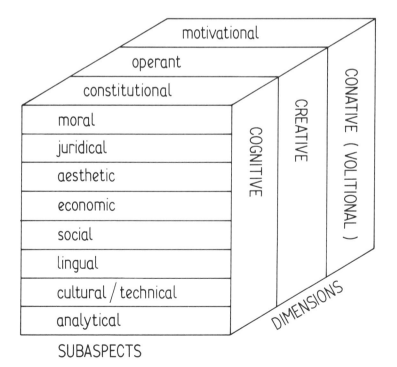

Early psychology

It is obvious that, if such an intricate model of man were valid, the doctrine of evolution would be very implausible. If man exhibits an organizational level called the spiritive structure, which cannot be reduced to lower structures, and if even the lower structures in man essentially differ from the corresponding structures in lower organisms, the idea of evolution from lower kingdoms cannot account for man's origin. This is the reason that scholars in the humanities have tried, over and over again, to argue away the spiritive structure and sometimes even the sensitive structure. Those who have tried to absolutize the perceptive structure we will call 'perceptivists', and those who have tried to absolutize the sensitive structure we will call 'sensitivists'. In order to understand what they have undertaken we have to follow a little of the history of psychology.

Experimental psychology as we know it today could only originate after (a) 'experiment' had been invented (sixteenth century), and (b) the natural sciences (providing knowledge about the physical and biotic structures of man) had been sufficiently developed (seventeenth and eighteenth centuries). It is no wonder, therefore, that the forerunners of psychology in the nineteenth century were physicists, physiologists and physicians. One of them, Gustav Fechner, wrote in 1860 a pioneering book, *Elements of Psychophysics,* which could be called the first experimental-psychological work. This book, however, clearly breathed the spirit of Darwin's *The Origin of Species,* that had appeared one year before. What was true of Fechner also applied to all early pioneers of psychology. They were all perceptivists or sensitivists who, under the influence of evolutionism, believed that the human mind could be explained entirely in physical or biotic terms.

Fechner had launched the experimental-psychological method, but it was Wilhelm Wundt (1832-1920) who founded a complete, new science on this method. In 1873/4 he published his pioneering book *Principles of Physiological Psychology.*[8] Wundt, too, was a thorough Darwinist, who consistently sought to explain the human mind in terms of remote animal origins. He and his followers saw psychology as the study of the human consciousness; they were called *structuralists* because they tried to analyse the structure and the elements of consciousness. His method was that of *introspection:* systematic self-analysis by experimental subjects; observation of changes within consciousness arising from different sensory stimuli. However, precisely because of their evolutionary prejudices, other investigators disagreed with this method because it could not be used for animals and small children. Therefore, it was impossible to learn about the *development* of consciousness, (the development from baby to adult, or the development from animal to human), and that is exactly what Darwinist psychologists did want to learn. Just as biologists were occupied with the changing *functions* of organs during the presumed evolutionary process, some psychologists wanted to know how the function of consciousness had developed during the continuous struggle for existence in evolution. These psychologists were called *functionalists*; the great American philosopher and psychologist William James (1842-1910) was their leader. They did not discard introspection entirely, but they were the first to introduce other kinds of experiments, namely, observation of *behaviour* in children and animals. By not asking subjects what they experienced *inwardly*, but by observing how subjects responded *outwardly*, they believed to be able to build a more 'objective' psychology than the structuralists.

Psychoanalysis and behaviourism

In the meantime, in Europe a totally different and independent school of psychology was developed by the psychiatrist Sigmund Freud (1856-1939). But in one respect he agreed with the former ones: he too was a convinced and consistent Darwinist. Already during his studies he was strongly attracted by the theories of Darwin, and it was said of him later that the revolution brought about by Darwin in biology was brought about by Freud in psychology.[9] He arrived at his *'psychoanalytic'* doctrine not through experiments but through observations on neurotic patients. Radically, he maintained that in psychology it was not first the conscious that matters, but a deeper and far more influential 'layer' in human personality, the 'unconscious'. If Wundt and James were more or less perceptivists, Freud was a clear-cut and fervent sensitivist. According to him, man's behaviour is largely determined by dark, hidden forces: sensitive impulses and 'repressed' emotions, largely formed through childhood conflicts between his impulsive (particularly sexual) lusts and the taboos of his environment.[10] Later, he extended these ideas to a full, evolutionary theory about the human *Id, Ego* and *Super-Ego*.[11] The Id belonged to the 'oldest, animal' part of the human brain; the Ego was a later evolutionary development from the evolved cerebral cortex; but man was still largely dominated by the 'animal' Id. The idea of the Oedipus Complex is another famous evolutionary doctrine of Freud, based on certain speculations (since refuted) about primitive cultures of cave men.

For Freud, all these ideas formed an almost unassailable life and world-view, indissolubly connected with his materialistic and evolutionistic views. His theories have exerted an enormous effect upon Western thinking, comparable with those of Darwin and Marx. Concepts like repression, inhibition, frustration, Freudian slip, the unconscious, have become commonplace amongst us. Also Freud's conceited writings about religion[12] — which he considered to be a mental disorder — have strongly contributed to the dechristianization of the Western world. Moreover, Freud has been the psychologist who perhaps is most responsible for the fact that in our century the concepts of real moral guilt and personal responsibility have largely lost their value. Man has been presented as being at the mercy of unconscious forces from within and conditioned by the severity of parents and society, for none of which he is responsible. Christian psychology, on the contrary, emphasizes that each man is personally responsible towards God and all derived authorities, even if unconscious forces do play a certain role (see below).

After Western Europe and America, let us now look at Russia. Around 1900, Ivan Pavlov (1849-1936) began his famous studies of 'reflexes' in animals. He showed how innate reflexes (unconditional responses to certain stimuli) could be made dependent on certain new, conditional stimuli and thereby become conditioned reflexes.[13] Pavlov was a convinced materialist and evolutionist, who explicitly placed his

results within the framework of his world-view. He trium-
phantly declared that, to interpret his conditioning experiments, it was not necessary to appeal to some kind of
'consciousness'. He maintained that the whole of human
mental life could be explained mechanically in terms of
conditioned reflexes. This is a very outspoken example of
perceptivism! If there *were* such things as mental phenomena,
they were, Pavlov asserted, only epiphenomena, which
(should) play no role in psychological interpretation.

When the results of Pavlov's work became known in
America, it was enthusiastically hailed by the functionalists,
and particularly by the founder of the new school of
behaviourism. In 1913 John Broadus Watson (1878-1958)
proclaimed his view that psychologists should finally break
with any concept of 'consciousness', because, for him,
psychology is a purely objective (!), experimental branch of
the natural sciences.[14] Things like consciousness, mental
states, volition, representations etc. simply cannot be described scientifically. By contrast behaviour *can* — and in purely
physiological terms at that! By discarding and denying all
mental concepts, Watson hoped to purify psychology of all
philosophical prejudices. But he did not realize that he himself
was simply caught in another (materialistic, evolutionistic)
world-view. One thing is true: Watson was very consistent in
his new conception. For instance, according to him there was
nothing mental in 'thinking'; it is nothing else than a kind of
inaudible speaking and involves slight muscular movements
in larynx, tongue and lips. 'Emotions' can be reduced entirely
to secretions in certain glands. Man essentially is 'nothing
but' a robot. Even the 'noblest' sensitive reactions of man are
based on 'nothing but' conditioned reflexes. This is perceptivistic 'nothing-buttism' (reductionism) at its most extreme.

Humanistic psychology

In the 1920s, the school of Watson dominated the whole of
American psychology; but in the 1930s, people began to see
that his view was too far-fetched. Many psychologists
'repented' from radical behaviourism, and other psychologists
developed a more moderate form, 'neo-behaviourism', of

which B.F. Skinner is the most famous representative. But more important is the fact that, after (sensitivistic) psycho-analysis and (perceptivistic) behaviourism, an entirely new school was developed in the 1950s. The leader of this school was the American psychologist Abraham Maslow (1908-1970).[15] This school had the great merit that it perceived the narrow-mindedness of both perceptivism and sensitivism; as a so-called 'third force psychology' it confronted both psychoanalysis and behavourism. Maslow blamed the be-haviourists for acting as if rats and pigeons could serve as a kind of simplified 'model of man'. According to him, much human behaviour is totally unique and cannot be reduced to the behaviour of rats, or even apes. Think of fire-making, tool-making, speaking, abstract thinking, creative social be-haviour, art, science, morals, religion. But Maslow also had a bone to pick with the psychoanalysts. He maintained that there is no evidence at all that all human behaviour could be reduced to irreflective drives or childhood conflicts. It is impossible to understand the behaviour of healthy people from the observations of psychiatrists on mentally disordered people, as Freud tried to do. The behaviourist finds his model in the animal, the psychoanalyst finds his in the patient. 'Well,' says Maslow, 'I want to start from healthy man. Psychology should finally become a real psychology *of man.*' Therefore, he called his approach '*humanistic psychology*'.

According to Maslow, a 'healthy person' is one who has realized all his inner potentials through a process of 'self-actualization'. To arrive at this, man has to satisfy his needs, and this in a well-defined hierarchic order. First, the physical needs (eating, drinking, sleeping, etc.) have to be satisfied before higher needs are felt. These higher needs are first those of security, safety and stability. Subsequently come the needs of affection and belongingness, then the needs of esteem and respect and finally the needs of self-actualization. This strong emphasis on 'needs' is evidence that Maslow, too, has not really overcome the limitations of Darwinistic thinking. He does not really arrive at that which is so characteristic of man: not his (mainly sensitive) needs, but his spiritive features. And above all, Maslow never touches that which is most essential for man, namely his heart, or his religious relation to God or to idols (see below). In a typically humanistic way, Maslow places man in the centre, together with the satisfaction of his self-oriented needs and his self-actualization. In Christianity, on the contrary, it is the realization and the development of a relationship with God, and the new life in Christ, that are central. In Christian life, the highest 'need' is the development of this communion with the Father and the Son.

So far, psychologists had not had much of an eye for the higher, spiritive faculties of man. This is easily understandable, for in the evolutionist point of view such faculties are difficult to account for. Therefore, as long as psychology was under the strong influence of Darwinism and naturalism, and thus remained immature, concepts like 'cognition' were simply taboo. For more than half a century, the grip of Darwinism kept psychology from maturing. However, the spiritive factors cannot be denied *ad infinitum;* they simply forced themselves on the investigators.

Cognitive psychology

One of the first who considered this matter was Robert S. Woodworth, who already in the 1920s refused to abolish the mental element as behaviourists required. In one of his books,[16] he extended the behaviourist formula S→R (S= stimulus; R=response) by adding the factor O for organism: S→O→R. This concept of 'organism' has to be taken in the broadest sense, thereby allowing for sensitive and spiritive factors. Another pioneer of what later would be called 'cognitive psychology'[17] was the neo-behaviourist Edward C. Tolman (1886-1959), who for this vague concept of 'organism' introduced the term 'intervening variables': S→IV→R. These variables included such 'anti-behaviourist' concepts as purposiveness and insight, unfortunately called 'cognitive' factors. In a pioneering book,[18] Tolman explained the results of his experiments which point to 'goal-directed' behaviour of rats in labyrinths. A rat, learning to find its way in a labyrinth, discovers how to avoid all blind alleys and learns to find the shortest way to the alluring food. This indicates that the rat is not only conditioned to carry out a series of separate movements but, as a road to a goal, learns a 'procedure', or a 'cognitive map'. It is not the stimuli themselves but this 'cognitive map' that, according to Tolman, determines the eventual responses of the animal.

Although these investigations refute the perceptivism of behaviourism, they still do not point out the cognitive differences between animals and man, which are so important in a creationist psychology. Within the scope of this lecture, I can only give a few examples, of which language is one of the most interesting. Psychologists have expressed new interest in language since Noam Chomsky's sensational book *Syntactic Structures* (1957).[19] We take 'language' here in the broadest sense as comprising all means by which people 'communicate': this includes words, gestures, grimaces, numbers, traffic signs, flags, etc. Language always uses 'communication signs', by which we mean that 'this' (sign, symbol) stands for (indicates, means, symbolizes) 'that'. This word stands for that concept; this number stands for that numerical value; this traffic sign stands for that prohibition, etc.

Psycholinguists want to know how people talk, how language functions as a means of communication between people, how languages are learned, from what psychological background new concepts and words arise, where slips come from, etc. Someone who 'speaks' (or writes) has 'coded' his thoughts in linguistic symbols with the help of Broca's area (one of the brain areas). Someone who listens (or reads) 'decodes' these words with the help of Wernicke's brain area. These linguistic brain centres are absolutely unique to man. Therefore animals do not know this kind of spiritive communication. Of course, they do 'communicate' in many ways (movements, grimaces, sounds, scents, touches), but that which is called 'communication' in animals is rigidly bound to the perceptive and sensitive structures. Therefore animals cannot creatively alter and extend their 'language'; they lack a spiritive structure for that. Therefore, animals know nothing of 'culture'. Extensive experiments with chimpanzees, both concerning the learning of spoken words or the learning of a gesture-language, have confirmed that these animals cannot learn language in the human sense of the word.[20]

Why is it, then, that children do learn their mother language so fast and so well? Infants learn the ground structure of even the most complicated languages within one and a half or two years, and that almost without any conscious, systematic instruction. How do children learn to pick up separate words in a stream of sounds, to group newly learned words into new phrases without any help, to associate words with concepts? Psychologists have recently given the only possible answer: people do, and chimpanzees do not, have at their disposal a special innate aptitude for languages, a 'Linguistic Acquisition Device (or System)'. Now this answer seems self-evident, but in reality it represents a little revolution in psychological thought. The Dutch (evolutionist) psychologists Duijker & Dudink wrote, 'Anyone looking over the tradition of psycholinguistic research ought to be impressed with this trend. Here, something is done which only recently was still considered to be something entirely unscientific, viz. to make a *fundamental* distinction between animal and man. This is the more striking because some psychologists, now having been forced by the facts to accept a linguistic acquisition device, did not only originate from the behaviourist school but also adhered to a conditioning theory of linguistic acquisition. This development — that may well be stamped revolutionary — is, for a great part, to be attributed to the influence of Chomsky.'[21]

Language is one of the most characteristic features of the spiritive structure. I referred already to the linguistic creativity of man, by which he is able to apply the infinite possibilities of language in endless variations, that is, to produce continually new phrases, never heard before, but still immediately understood by those who hear them. Language also clearly exhibits a cognitive aspect. Our thought and knowledge is, for the greater part, inconceivable without language: thought largely takes place through, and knowledge largely consists in the form of, lingual concepts. One of the most interesting questions in animal research is in how far animals know 'concepts'. Perhaps animals do not speak with one another because they have 'nothing to say', that is, because they do not know a variety of differentiated, and especially abstract concepts. Insofar as animals have communication systems, the elements of those systems probably never function as symbols for concepts that exist independently of the communicative situation. That is, it is doubtful whether animal communicative *signals* ever function as *symbols,* in other words, whether animals can 'think'. Thirdly, we discover a volitional aspect in human language. If I would like to explain what is, say, a typewriter, I have to give spiritive commands to certain brain centres to produce the appropriate terms to provide the description needed. Of course, perceptive and sensitive factors play a (sometimes important) role in linguistic acquisition and speech. But it has clearly turned out to be impossible to *reduce* this and other spiritive phenomena entirely to the lower structures.

Existentialist psychology

Of course, there are still materialist behaviourists today, but they form a minority. In practice, many psychologists do not care very much about their 'view of man'. They accept both physical and mental phenomena, avoid trying to reduce the one to the other and do not care about the relation between the two, or about the 'essence' of man. A great exception to this are the existentialists, like Karl Jaspers (1883-1969),[22] Martin Heidegger (1889-1976)[23] and Jean-Paul Sartre (1905-1980).[24] Their view of life definitely does demand a conception of the 'essence' of man. They strongly emphasize the total, concrete man, his uniqueness, his authenticity, his true, full 'existence' in the midst of an incomprehensible, absurd world, in which man has to learn to make choices. Incidentally, their view is, just like that of psychoanalysis and humanistic psychology, more a life- and world-view than an empirical science, but it has still exerted a considerable influence on modern psychology.

Over against psychoanalysts and behaviourists, existentialists have emphasized that human consciousness cannot be reduced to physico-chemical processes but is only 'carried' by such processes. A Christian can agree with this, but more important are the points on which he differs. According to existentialists, the consciousness (or the mind) is completely *free.* Human behaviour is not determined by our molecules but by our free choices. Man only *lives,* he only truly 'exists', if his liberty is not limited by anything. But with this the Christian cannot agree, because this would mean that man is 'free' from the ordinances laid down by the Creator and given by him in his Word. The existentialist idolizes the freely developing, evolving mind of man. The drives of the psychoanalyst and the conditioned reflexes of the behaviourist are here replaced by free, spiritual, creative self-development. But this is not the answer either. Man's spiritive life cannot be reduced to drives and reflexes; but neither can it be elevated to a free and independent mind, hovering above mechanical matter. Spiritive life is definitely free, but not in licentiousness. It is subject *not* just to drives or reflexes but to man's *heart*. It is in this heart that man is either oriented towards God and his commandments (and thus really free!) or oriented towards slavery to idols, be it idols within man (e.g., his drives) or in his environment, either material (like money) or spiritual (like demons).

Man is subject not only to natural laws in the lower structures but to divine *norms* in the spiritive structure: logical, technical, lingual, social, economic, aesthetic, juridical, ethical and pistical norms. It was not man who invented them, although he has discovered and positivized them, but they were laid down in creation ordinances by God. True liberty is not independence of, but subjection to, these divine norms. *All* psychological schools mentioned misapprehend this 'vertical' relation of man to God. Psychologists want to understand something of man, but their evolutionistic prejudices prevent them seeing the 'essence' of man, which is to be found in his 'heart'.

The concept of heart

This concept of 'heart' plays a great role in Christian psychology as I visualize it. It is essential to see that man is *not* fully described by the five hierarchic structures I mentioned before, because they do not indicate how and where the *unity* of man is to be found. We postulate in man a 'centre', a 'focus', in which all his aspects and structures come together and find their unity and coherence. This 'point' cannot be located in the body, and is not even scientifically analysable. The miracle that is 'man' is too great, too profound for that; man is not only the greatest of God's works of creation but also incomparable with the other creatures. We can only try to speak about the heart in figurative language. From earliest times on, people have called it the soul, the spirit, the mind, the ego, or personality. I perfer the term which the Bible employs, namely the *heart,* which, of course, is also a figure. The Bible hardly ever uses this word to describe the physical heart, however.

In non-Christian views of man, people have usually sought this ego in one of the hierarchic structures. The spiritive (the 'mind') or the sensitive ('feeling'), or even biotic life or pure matter, were declared to be the essence of man. We have seen how people were led to these errors under the influence of evolutionism. However, the ego or heart is *not* one of the 'parts', structures or aspects of man. Just like the centre of a

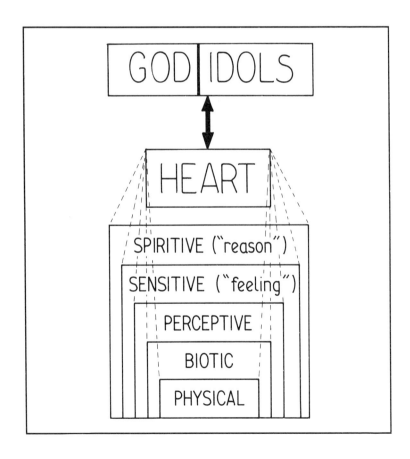

circle is not one of the points on the circle circumference, the heart is not a certain 'part' of man but the 'point' in which all 'parts' of man converge and unify. Indeed, it is in this 'point' that man transcends all his temporal 'parts' and structures! Therefore, man has an ego, and animals have not. Precisely because man has an ego, a heart, he is an 'eternal being', for it is in this ego that man is oriented towards the transcendent, towards God or the idols. Many temporal, transitory structures can be discerned in man, but, in his ego, man transcends all that is transient and time-limited. In the heart, the whole man, being the image of God, stands before God.

The heart is therefore the deepest inner self, the truest and most essential point in human personality. In this way, the heart has a tremendous *religious* significance. 'Religion' (serving and worshipping God *or* idols) is not just the activity of one human structure, of a 'part' of man. Religion is a matter of the total man, therefore of the heart. As a creature, man originally had an intense bond with, and orientation towards, his Creator and Preserver. By the Fall, this bond has been profoundly disturbed, but by redemption it is restored. In his heart, man is most 'human'; here we find his essence, basically inaccessible to (secular) psychology and known, not by feelings or intellect but by the (regenerated) heart itself.

In this basic idea of the heart, the distinction between evolutionist and creationist psychology is most conspicuous. Evolutionism, maintaining that man has evolved from impersonal animals, can never account for the personality (in the sense of personhood) of man. Because man has a heart, he is what we call a *person*. The whole of man's spiritive life is governed by and from his heart. In and through this heart, man is therefore *responsible* to God. As we saw in the case of Freud, evolutionist psychology cannot really account for 'responsibility'. Man ultimately is not governed by drives, instincts and reflexes but by spiritive 'acts', placed under divine norms and going out from the heart. Because this takes place differently in each human, each one is not only a person but a unique personality, called to give shape, in his own unique way, to his responsibility towards God.

Human personalities

It is quite remarkable that the *term* 'person' is not in the Bible, although it did occur amongst the ancient Greeks. However, the *concept* of a 'person' is not Greek at all but fully biblical. Insofar as modern evolutionists use the concept of a 'person' they do so in the manner of the old (evolutionist!) Greeks, not in the biblical sense. The Greeks did not possess a correct idea of the person because they did not have a correct idea of God; the former follows directly from the latter. If we do not apprehend what it means that God is 'personal', we do not apprehend what we ourselves are as 'persons'. The gods of the ancient Greeks and Romans were personal but not infinite, like the God of the Bible. They were not creators, and they were not morally perfect either. Over against the quarrelling and immoral gods of the Olympus, the Greek needed to feel little responsibility or guilt. When it was a matter of sin and penitence, the Greek fell back rather upon his older, natural religion with its unpredictable, whimsical, blind natural forces to which man was subject. No one could beat Fate, not even the gods of the Olympus! The Greeks tried to picture the influence of this blind Fate in their tragedies, in which Fate plays a central role. In those tragedies, the actors wore certain masks, called *persona* in Latin. Those who wore those masks depicted certain characters, 'persons'; but these 'persons' in reality were at the mercy of the blind, capricious forces of Fate. In fact, these 'persons' *had* no character. What happened to them was not a consequence of their own actions, good or evil, that is, it was not their own responsibility, but the result of incalculable forces entirely outside them. It could not be otherwise; the gods of the Greek, being unable to match Fate, were simply not great enough. Therefore the Greek 'person' was not great, not 'personal' enough.

This is strikingly similar to the views of the modern evolutionist humanities. Man has again become a sport of fortune, at the mercy of natural selection and other situational factors outside him as well as of drives and instincts (inherited from his animal ancestors) within him. The well-known Gestalt psychologist Kurt Lewin (1890-1947) has studied the 'dynamic forces' in and around man which determine his behaviour.[25] He devised a complete 'field of forces' influencing human behaviour, and framed the personal factors (P) within man and the situational factors (S) around him in his famous formula B=ƒ (P , S) (B=behaviour). As long as cognitive factors are left out of P, such a person is no better off than the ancient Greek 'pseudo-persons'. Lewin did include cognitive factors, however, and this was a big step forward compared with the psychoanalysts and behaviourists, who had never lifted themselves above the level of the Greek tragedy. That which someone *knows*, or believes he knows, about himself or his environment was introduced by Lewin as a principal factor in human behaviour. This was an important insight — but it was not enough. It still leaves out the most important factor in human behaviour. Man is not in the first place a cognitive, creative or volitional being; he is not in the first place a logical, a historical, a lingual, a social, an economic, an aesthetic, a juridical, a moral or even a pistical being, however important and humanly unique these aspects may be. Man is first a *religious* being, serving either God or idols. The principal factor determining his behaviour is the religious state of his heart, involving such important notions as responsibility, guidance, guilt and forgiveness, retribution and reward, good and evil.

This idea of a person, which in fact is familiar to Western man (including the evolutionists), is not derived from Greek thought but from the Old Testament. There we find a personal *and* infinite God, the Creator and Preserver of man, who tells him, 'I have made you, and I will tell you how you should live. I give you my commandments because I love you, and because I desire your good' (cf. e.g. Deut.7:8-11). Man is thus a *real person*, whose personality is derived from God's personality — he is the image of God. He receives from this God a 'framework' (God's commandments), in order that he may function in an optimal way, and receive strength to work out his responsibility.

Psychotherapy and the gospel

This response to God's commandments is a strictly individual matter. *Individuality* is a notion that plays a considerable part in the Bible, but an inferior role in both ancient and modern evolutionary thought. Both for the Greeks and for consistent evolutionists, the individual can only have value as a representative of the human race. He is only an insignificant wheel in the big machine of nature, a sport of the waves of time and chance. Man is essentially *nothing*. For God, man is never nothing. Man is a sinner by nature, he is an enemy of God, badly needing forgiveness, redemption, reconciliation — but he is not nothing. God loves him and stretches out his hand to him, in order that his highest creature may again find its destiny and fulfilment, namely life with God through Christ.

Psychoanalysts have pointed out how anxieties, guilt feelings, depressions, psychosomatic disorders, self-condemnation etc. may be the consequence of disturbed sensitive factors. But it has been their greatest mistake to think that those disorders can *always* be reduced to these factors. They often — and in a sense always — have to do with man's relation with God. Guilt feeling, then, has to do with real, concrete guilt. Self-condemnation is no delusion, but real and right. Anxieties and depressions are real for they are based on the realization of the future judgement of God. Of course, we know that there are also religious delusions. We also realize that religious factors are sometimes strongly mixed with perceptive, sensitive and spiritual factors; evangelists and pastors ought to know that. However, there is also real mental misery which is first determined by man's relation with the transcendent. To put it differently, it is basically misery of the *heart*. Someone finding himself in such misery does not need psychotherapy, but the gospel of Jesus Christ, who has borne the judgement of sin on Calvary's cross as the Substitute of all who believe in him. Christian psychology is not of theoretical interest only; refuting evolutionist psychology is not of scientific interest only. It is in the interest of thousands of needy people, treated as repairable robots, but who are really the image of God and who can be delivered from their fear and guilt. This is the highest aim of creationist psychology: to further the re-creation of people by the Spirit of God through the blood of Christ.

References

1. Ch.R. Darwin, *The Origin of Species* (1859; repr. Dent, London 1928, 1967), p.461f.
2. E.G. Bewkes, H.B. Jefferson, E.T. Adams & H. A. Brautigam, *Experience, Reason and Faith* (Harper & Br., New York 1940), p.549.
3. See my *Psychologie: Een christelijke kijk op het mentale leven* (Buijten & Schipperheijn, Amsterdam 1984), pp.152f., 169f., 175f.
4. C.H. Judd, *Educational Psychology* (Houghton Mifflin Co., New York), p.15.
5. See my *Psychologie*.
6. I have coined the word 'spiritive' to avoid religious connotations involved in the word 'spiritual'.
7. G.Th. Fechner, *Elemente der Psychophysik* (Breitkopf & Härtel, Leipzig 1860).
8. W. Wundt, *Grundzüge der physiologischen Psychologie* (Engelmann Verlag, Leipzig 1873/4).
9. S. Freud, *Gesammelte Werke* (Imago Publ. Co., London 1941), vol. XIV, p.34; E. Jones, *Sigmund Freud: Life and Work* II (Hogarth Press, London 1955), p.471.
10. S. Freud, *Drei Abhandlungen zur Sexualtheorie* (1905; see *Gesammelte Werke*, vol. V, p.27-132).
11. *Idem, Das Ich und das Es* (1923; vol. XIII, p.235-290).
12. *Idem, Totem und Tabu* (1913); *Die Zukunft einer Illusion* (1927); *Das Unbehagen in der Kultur* (1930) (vol. IX; vol. XIV, pp.323-380; pp.419-506).
13. I. Pavlov, *Conditioned Reflexes: An Investigation of the Physiological Activity of the Cerebral Cortex* (Oxford Univ. Press, London 1927).
14. J.B. Watson, 'Psychology as the Behaviourist Views It', *Psychological Review* 20 (1913), pp.158-177.
15. See A. Maslow, *Motivation and Personality* (Harper & Row, New York 1954) and many other books.
16. R.S. Woodworth, *Psychology: A Study of Mental Life* (Holt, New York 1921).
17. See, as a standard work, U. Neisser, *Cognitive Psychology* (Appleton-Century-Crofts, New York 1967).
18. E.C. Tolman, *Purposive Behaviour in Animals and Men* (Appleton-Century-Crofts, New York 1932).
19. N. Chomsky, *Syntactic Structures* (Mouton, The Hague 1957).
20. C. Hayes, *The Ape in Our House* (Harper & Row, New York 1951); R.A. Gardner & B.T. Gardner, 'Teaching Sign Language to a Chimpanzee', *Science* 165 (1969), pp.664-672; H.S. Terrace, *Nim* (A.A. Knoft, New York 1979).

21. H.C.J. Duijker & A.C. Dudink, *Leerboek der psychologie* (Wolters-Noordhoff, Groningen 1976), p.305f.
22. K. Jaspers, *Psychologie der Weltanschauungen* (Springer, Berlin 1919); *Philosophie* I-III (Ibid. 1932).
23. M. Heidegger, *Sein und Zeit* (Max Niemeyer Verlag, Halle 1927).
24. J.-P. Sartre, *L'être et le néant* (Gallimard, Paris 1943); *Esquisse d'une théorie des émotions* (Hermann, Paris 1948).
25. K. Lewin, *Principles of Topological Psychology* (McGraw-Hill, New York); *Psychological Forces* (Durham Univ. Press, Durham 1938).

5.

The impact of evolution on historiography

Dennis W. Cheek

Man's preoccupation with change over time and his place in time has given rise to a pervading historical consciousness. Ask a twentieth-century Western man about the meaning of any particular institution, social event, or even personal event, and the chances are good he will give you an answer brimming with history. Libraries filled with books titled *A History of...* reinforce this perception. This influential view of the twentieth-century world exists due to man's loss of belief in any type of absolute knowledge. The supposed relativistic world we live in has left man without answers to questions of ultimate purpose and meaning. So man has focused his attention more on questions which have 'what', 'when' and 'how' as points of analysis. Queries as to 'why', or ultimate purpose, are sidestepped in favour of answers showing change over time. This is done in the mistaken belief that somehow these historical evidences of change can substitute for the ultimate answers that our forefathers sought to formulate.

The meaning of history

Ask a modern man about the *meaning* of history and with little hesitation he will tell you history has no meaning. If he possesses more philosophical acumen he will cite in his defence names such as Hempel, Becker, Popper, Dilthey,

Collingwood, Croce and Beard. If you could ask an ancient
Hebrew the same question, he would speedily reply that
history is the stage for the working out of God's plan for his
chosen people. Modern man remembers the past in an
attempt to find his place in the present and in the 'flow' of
things. The ancient Hebrew remembered the past (as do his
modern counterparts — the orthodox Jew, Moslem and
Christian) in order to understand, albeit dimly, the progressive outworking of his Lord's plan. This concern with *Where is
History Going?* as John Warwick Montgomery styles it, is tied
up with the theist's view that history's ultimate purpose is
found in the mind of God. It is sketchily revealed in God's
revelation to man and never found inherent and deducible in
solely human affairs. With his emphasis on absolute truth and
pattern in history, the modern theist is as far removed from his
non-theist contemporary as the ancient Hebrew was from the
ancient Greek (Auerbach).

The role, then, of presuppositions in the study and writing
of history cannot be ignored. The historian's presuppositions
affect not only his choice of materials (since in the broadest
sense 'all of the past is history') but how he puts those
materials together into a comprehensive narrative framework.
This can be seen readily in the historiography of Israel and
the history of Christianity as two related examples. The
writings of Jewish authors, like Josephus, and Christian
authors like Justin Martyr, Augustine and Eusebius, fall into
one basic group. These theocentric accounts of Israel's history
and the spread of Christianity contrast sharply with accounts
that survive from 'pagan' writers of antiquity, such as
Manetho of the third century B.C. Exceptions to such an easy
division do admittedly exist, such as the writings of Heca-
taeus, Theophrastus, Megasthenes and Clearchus, but what
emerges clearly is that philosophical presuppositions radically
condition what historians choose to follow in constructing
detailed accounts of the history of the Jews.

These ancient writers often made their apologetic concerns
known to the reader. Eusebius in his *Historia ecclesiastica* (312-
324 A.D.) is frank about his apologetic aim to show that it was
through the providence of God that a Christian empire was
brought into existence by Constantine. He admits that he
will 'introduce into this history in general only those events

which may be useful first to ourselves and afterward, to posterity'. One should not conclude that early Christian writers were ignorant of pagan myths or history. The chronological scheme of Sextus Julius Africanus of the third century and those who followed in his footsteps amply demonstrates that they were not. The writing of history was undertaken in the light of eternity and only those items considered germane to the working out of God's plan in history were included. Thus Augustine's *De civitate Dei* in the fifth century plays down the role of secular history, subsuming it under the providential scheme in which the heavenly city triumphs ultimately over the earthly city of man. This becomes even clearer in Orosius, Augustine's pupil, whose seminal work, *Historiarum libri VII adversus paganos* exerted a greater influence on medieval views of history than the works of his mentor. By the time we reach Bede's *Historia ecclesiastica gentis Anglorum* in the eighth century, it is considered self-evident in Western Europe that God does work in human history, 'his wonders to perform'.

It is not until the Renaissance that there begins a questioning of such a providential approach to history in the West. The seeds of such a change in view may be found in Valla's critical attempt to reconstruct the original text of the Bible using philology, history, palaeography and an implicit philosophy as guides. Erasmus went one step further in arguing that theology, the queen of the sciences, had to give way to grammar. He tempered his suggestion by severely limiting the role of the grammarians, and still argued for a Christocentric piety to pervade one's work. Changes in such an approach to the Bible, and consequently the history of Israel and the Christian church, reached their critical peak with the ideas of Julius Wellhausen in the late nineteenth century and his pupils (Noth,Lods). A conservative reaction to such radical schemes of historical reconstruction has set in, although the impact of documentary and form-critical approaches to biblical studies has continued, tempered yet unabated (Albright, Bright, Bruce, DeVaux, Wood). This is in spite of the fact that the basis for such critical reconstructions is manifestly weak or fictitious (Polzin in Campbell Jr and Boling). Often the old explanations and theories are dressed up in new garb and continue to figure prominently in

accounts of the history of Israel and the growth of the
Christian church (Hayes and Miller, Hermann, Momigliano).

Examples of the role of presuppositions in the handling of
historical data abound. Particularly striking are many historians' attempts to ignore completely the role of Christianity
as a force in human history. Even such avowed atheists as
Marx and Engels took cognizance of religion's role in society
and of Christianity's role, in particular, in shaping historical
events, although economic determinism remained for them
the major force (Lee). This is especially apparent when the
origin of modern scientific enterprise is considered and results
in an extremely warped view. Fortunately some careful
historians of science with biblically oriented presuppositions
have recently redressed some of the imbalance in this arena
(Hooykaas, Jaki, Klaaren, Russell).

Evolutionism in historical writing

With these introductory comments in view, we shall focus our
attention on the role of evolutionism as a philosophical
presupposition in historical writing. It is my intent to
demonstrate that evolutionism in historiography clearly pre-
ceded Darwinism and indeed any biological theory of origins
that could be judged quasi-scientific. This is because naturalistic views of man's origin, society and culture necessarily
entail a gradual evolutionary progression, whether unilinear,
multilinear, cyclic, spiralling, or some mixture thereof. While
this thesis could be illustrated and amplified by numerous
examples, I have chosen to focus on the origin of man's
culture and civilization. Historians, prehistorians and others
have speculated and argued about this subject and attempted
to verify their theories using historical and archaeological
data.

Our modern terms 'culture' and 'civilization' are, of course,
derived from Latin. '*Cultura*' referred to the cultivation of the
soil, while '*civis*' indicated the status of citizenship. These
terms imply a coalescence of various related activities such as
sedentarism, political process, technology, socialization, col-
lectivism, and so on. What exactly constitutes 'culture' is by
no means easy to define. Kroebner and Kluckhorn found no

less than 164 different definitions up to 1952! What all writers on 'culture' have basically agreed is that some combination of these various characteristics constitutes a culture. Persistence of cultures over a period of time and space generally is associated with the word 'civilization'. How culture and civilization came about 'in the beginning' has provided no unanimity of opinion.

Ancient times

Ancient Sumerian mythological literature seems to indicate that human culture arose by direct intervention of the gods and evolved from that point in stages, from hunting to pastoralism to grain agriculture (Lutz). Hindu, Mayan, Egyptian, Babylonian and Chinese literature is replete with references to the endless cycles of existence. No straightforward account of man's culture and civilization survives except for scattered references to the belief that the gods instituted the first culture (Jaki, 1974). It is only among the Greeks and the Hebrews that a coherent, systematic attempt is made to account for the origin of man's culture and civilization.

Cicero made Herodotus 'the father of history' and most historiographers have followed his lead in crediting the first true histories to the Greeks. A small, but vocal, minority have argued that the ancient Hebrews deserve the title. The Greeks distinguished three types of what we would today call historical writing: history, biography and antiquities. 'History' aimed to give a true story but was governed in its presentation by the rules of rhetoric expounded by Isocrates, a generation before Aristotle. Moral lessons were to be stressed. The purpose of 'biography' was to praise and edify, often at the expense of the facts. 'Antiquities' involved the use of wider source materials such as language, ancient customs, religion and literature to demonstrate topically the origin and change of culture over time. Its supreme practitioner in antiquity was Varro (116-27 B.C.), who systematically surveyed Roman life. Many philosophers objected strenuously to the value of 'history' since it dealt with particulars and not generalities, and preferred the study of antiquities (Aristotle, *Poetics*).

The Greek poets and philosophers

The poets and philosophers are our sources for ideas concerning the origins of man's culture and civilization, since the historians of Greece concentrated on contemporary history. Hesiod represents what can be termed the degenerative view (Griffiths). He wrote that at the first the gods had made a race of people like themselves. There was freedom from pain, misery, fatigue and war. Eventually this race became the guardians of fortune and served as spiritual helpers of mankind. Next the gods fashioned a group of men who were inferior to the first, as silver is to gold. They refused to serve the gods, injured one another and consequently lived brief and violent lives. Zeus converted them into the spirits of the underworld. The next created group of men, Hesiod likened to bronze. They made war their way of life and exterminated themselves. The fourth group were constituted a company of heroes who brought a short but necessary respite from the degeneration. Hesiod believed that some of them lived in his own day in remote parts of the world. The fifth and final group, which Hesiod likened to iron, were his contemporaries. They experienced ceaseless work and suffering, children disobeyed their parents, the rich oppressed the poor and society was in the throes of endless power struggles. Hesiod, as a result, longed to leave the earth and join the gods.

In contrast to Hesiod's pessimism were the optimistic views of Democritus, Plato and Aristotle. Democritus believed the earliest people to be undisciplined, naked and ignorant of such civilizing influences as fire, shelter and agriculture. These people eventually congregated into small groups to protect themselves against beasts. Random speech sounds gave rise to language and different languages arose in parallel. Eventually they learned to use caves, build fire, store food and found enough comfort and leisure to develop music and the arts. Democritus dismissed the intervention of any supernatural beings in man's rise to civilization. Men had it in their own power to conquer the elements, control their own foibles and follies and develop a high state of culture.

Plato (*Protagoras,* 322) followed Democritus' views except that he ascribed religion and justice to supernatural intervention. In the *Laws* (III. 676-681) Plato described the restart of society after a world-wide deluge from which only a few shepherds survived. Using some clothing, containers and a few domesticated animals that survived the catastrophe, these men gathered in small groups. These families required no laws. Eventually as the groups grew in size and became tribes there were problems as different customs clashed. Arbiters were appointed and they selected those customs best suited to mankind as a whole. Upon acceptance by chiefs of the tribes, who met in conferences, these decisions became law.

Aristotle (*Politics*, I. 1-2,8; III. 4,9) refined Plato's sequence into three levels of social organization : (1) a patriarchal household, (2) the village and (3) the city or state. Alongside these institutions, Aristotle recognized three primary modes of subsistence: (1) nomadic pastoralism (the easiest); (2) hunting and fishing; and (3) agriculture. He did not correlate the levels of organization with modes of subsistence, nor did he suggest any evolutionary sequence. He ultimately believed man had been derived from the animal world. Yet he recognized man's ascendency, arguing, for example, that man is not the most intelligent of animals because he has hands (the view of Anaxogoras) but has hands because he is the most intelligent (*De partibus animalium*, 687a., 7-10).

As to the origin of religion, the ancient Greek poets and philosophers early ascribed it to man's own propensity to fashion gods in their own image (Xenophanes, 6th c. B.C.). This inventiveness was limited only by the tendency to project into the supernatural realm elements from familiar, everyday phenomena (Robinson). By the fifth century B.C., Critias (Plato's uncle), Democritus and Prodicus had argued extensively for a natural, gradual and essentially evolutionary development of man's religion.

The biblical view

The naturalistic, evolutionary views of the ancient Greek poets and philosophers can be contrasted with the supernaturalistic view of the ancient Hebrews. The Bible clearly presents man as having originated directly from the hands of God. He is endowed from the first with the ability to utilize language, categorize objects, form lasting social relationships, manipulate tools and presumably write (else how could he remember the names of all the animals?). He is in direct communication with God and still engages in continued communication after his fall. He is distinct from the animals and is able to think, rationalize and exercise judgement (not always correctly, but certainly independently of divine intervention). While the Bible provides useful data to frame an account of the origin of man and his culture, it emphatically does not provide a history (McCone). This is not a reflection on the Bible's integrity but rather a recognition of the nature of historical explanation. History is concerned with time and things related to time. God's creation stands outside of time in the sense that time is a human abstraction in which to arrange and integrate one's life. Attempts to fit the Bible stringently into a historical framework are doomed to fail not because the Bible is false in the historical information it gives us, but because the Bible, as God's revelation to man, stands both in and yet outside of time. Historians will search in vain for certain information that is standard fare in historical writing but not in the Bible. What it gives us is sufficient knowledge about the origin of man's culture and civilization but not exhaustive knowledge. This has to do with the focus of God's revelation to man. As Ephraim Speiser pointed out some time ago, the reader of the Bible is told where he can find other, complementary, aspects, viz. *The Book of the Wars of Yahweh* (Num. 21:14), *The Chronicle of Solomon* (1 Kings 11:41), *The Chronicles of the Kings of Israel* (1 Kings 14:19; 15:31; 16:5), or *The Chronicles of the Kings of Judah* (1 Kings 14:29; 15:7; 22:46).

It is on this basis that Origen of the third century A.D. derives certain technological aspects of man's culture (*Contra Celsum*, 6. 75-78,81). God created man with certain basic, biological needs. He endowed man with a rational mind to devise means of meeting those needs. Thus society and culture arose from man rationally and purposefully inventing husbandry, spinning, weaving, carpentry, etc. Nothing happened by chance in the scheme of Origen but man's culture is the result of deliberate, purposeful activity. He contrasts this with bee societies whose lack of rationality leads to a purely mechanical outcome. The fact that human societies differed was not due to some evolutionary sequence of accidental discoveries but rather due to the will of God being worked out in these cultures (*De Principiis*, 2.9).

Medieval figures like Otto, Bishop of Freising in Bavaria in the twelfth century, carry on this idea. Judged by many historians to be the most profound Christian philosophy of history in the Middle Ages, Otto's *Chronica* covered the history of the world down to A.D. 1146. While Otto reflected optimism in the value of history as a record of human progress, he grounded man's progress in rational thought and not in chance discoveries. Attempting to account for human achievements after the Flood, Otto credited man's cultural development to his Creator-endowed reason and to the wise and rational laws that man himself propounded.

Similar ideas occur in the writings of that towering figure of Islamic historiography, Ibn Khaldûn (see also Holt, Lambton, Lewis). Khaldûn completed in 1377 a multi-volume universal history which to this day has not been fully translated into English. Like Origen, Khaldûn started with biblically centred presuppositions. Consequently he warned against exact parallels between animal behaviour and human societies and institutions. Man's created rationality caused him naturally to seek a better standard of living. On this basis Khaldûn compares and contrasts two cultural types, the Bedouin (desert-dwelling pastoralists) and the sedentary (located in cities and using agriculture for subsistence). He derives the sedentary from the Bedouin type since men first obtained the bare necessities of life after the Flood. While the picture he paints of desert life is stark, Khaldûn believed it to be superior in terms of bravery, religious fervour, stamina and solidarity. Thus he rejected any type of progressive tendency that ignored man's degeneration due to sinfulness.

The Renaissance

With the arrival of the Renaissance a biblically centred view of man and his culture begins to disintegrate and a distinctly evolutionary mode of explanation is resurrected. The fact that Renaissance scholars looked to Greece and Rome for their models inevitably led to such a result. The very coining of the term 'Middle Ages' in the Renaissance by Bruni (*Historiae Florentini populi*) and Biondo (*Historiarum ab inclinatione Romanorum imperii decades*) was their way of denigrating a millennium of what they saw as prolonged decline, from the fall of the Roman Empire till the end of the fifteenth century. Valla, the Italian humanist, applied his rules of historical philology to reconstruct the correct usage of Latin words (*Elegantiae linguae latinae*, 1444). He argued that the meaning of words was not natural but dictated by changing conventions and history. A few years later he used the same methods to attempt to recover the original Greek version of the New Testament. This was primarily to correct the Latin Vulgate which the church had recognized as authoritative. He was the first to give voice to the idea that 'None of the words of Christ have come to us, for Christ spoke in Hebrew, and never wrote anything down.' Erasmus published Valla's corrections as *Annotationes* in 1505 and they provided the basis for Erasmus' New Testament Greek text and all new versions of the Bible in the sixteenth century.

The overall radical emendations of the humanist editors between 1400-1550 eventually spent themselves. Since these men destroyed many of the manuscripts they believed to be inferior, historians since the seventeenth century have spent much time and effort to reconstruct the manuscript versions of ancient texts available before 1400. It certainly can be argued that historiography as a systematic discipline had a still birth in the Renaissance after very promising beginnings, due to a preoccupation with tracing what were nothing but fanciful evolutionary explanations of change of texts over time.

Renaissance humanists were eager to suggest ideas as to the origins of man's culture and civilization. They worked within a framework of gradual yet inevitable progress of the human species. The majority of writers in the Middle Ages believed the ancients surpassed them in wisdom. The humanists from the fifteenth century argued that their times were a vast improvement of all that had gone before and a harbinger of continued improvement in the future. Thus Giordano Bruno argued in 1584 that man's marvellous inventions had lifted him out of his bestial nature (Imerti). Indeed, if progress were to continue uninterrupted, Bruno said, man would soon reach the status of a divine being.

Juan Luis Vives in 1531 followed the view of Lucretius that man's culture could best be accounted for by his instinct for self-preservation. Natural curiosity accounted for man's quest for knowledge. The first explicitly to place man's beginnings in pre-Adamic times, Vives starts his prehistory of social organization with a period of promiscuity. After sidestepping the problem of the origin of family life and marriage, Vives wrote that eventually families converged on certain localities and villages arose. Old men within the families served as patriarchal figures. As time went on, leaders were chosen with age as a minor factor and laws devised. After these villagers succeeded in providing for the necessities of life they turned to finding practical uses for natural objects. Universal laws of knowledge were arrived at and provided impetus to further discoveries. Eventually theoretical knowledge held sway as all the applied technology that could be found had appeared by Vives' own day. He goes on to speculate that perhaps the confused and contradictory ruminations of his own time might forestall any further progress but does not suggest a route out of the impasse.

An evolutionary progression of mankind is evident in the writings of Johann Boemus in 1520. Although starting his scenario after the exile from the Garden of Eden, Boemus' views show a low, naturalistic view of the pinnacle of God's creative ability. After the exile, humans dispersed throughout the world. They were ignorant of money, trade, shelter and any comforts. They dressed in bark, leaves or fur. Eventually, as discontent and fear grew, they congregated into communities, chose leaders, drew up laws and placed boundaries on the land. Man's discontent led him eventually to develop agriculture, handicrafts, means of conveyance and to domesticate animals.

The Enlightenment

By the time the seventeenth century dawned, much of the leading thinking of the age accepted that man began his earthly journey in a primitive state. John Locke, the eminent English social philosopher, argued in 1690 that 'In the beginning all the world was America' (Peardon). By this he meant that everyone at the dawn of human existence lived as the American Indians of his day. For Locke this entailed a natural equality between individuals, commonality of property and personal injuries limited to punishment for offences against society as a whole (i.e. the absence of personal conflicts). He contested Thomas Hobbes' belief that political organization was originated to restrain conflict. The source of political organization was man's desire to preserve human freedom and to enable the full range of man's social nature to develop. There were no innate ideas in the mind of man at the beginning (including the idea of God). Custom, more powerful than nature, dictated behavioural patterns and cultural beliefs of different societies.

Influential ideas concerning the origins of man's culture and civilization also emerged from the Friday night meetings of the Edinburgh Select Society, where Henry Home (Lord Kames), David Hume, Adam Smith and James Burnett, among others, met to exchange ideas on topics of common interest. Henry Home in his *Sketches of the History of Man* (1774) detailed in four massive volumes his views of the origin of man's culture and civilization. Using the comparative method of what would later be called ethology, Home attributed man's rise to civilization to his inability to defend himself individually (ideas similar to those of Lucretius and Vives). He linked man's early tribal state with man's animal heritage.

Home's history begins with the stage of hunting, fishing and collecting. Societies then domesticate animals they previously hunted for food and cultivate plants they previously picked in the wild. He argued that trade would also have to exist at this time since people would require some things nature could not provide. The barter system functioned well for a time but was eventually replaced by precious metals as media of exchange in order to regulate transactions. While man was initially autonomous, he quickly learned the benefits of cooperative activity. Increased interdependence came about due to developing trade and specialization in the means and modes of production. Increased contacts between groups prompted hostilities especially as subsistence patterns stabilized. Population pressures, the increased value of land, and man's natural hunger for greater luxuries led to warfare. Home concluded that the alleviation of these various social pressures by social engineering would lead to the continued progress of mankind.

Adam Ferguson, a fellow Scot, who started in the ministry

before turning to philosophy, reacted against much of the philosophical speculation of his contemporaries concerning early man (Forbes). He rejected the use of mythology of ancient and modern peoples as accurate 'documents' for historical reconstruction. He suggested that instead of arbitrarily selecting a few features of a living society that happened to match a writer's philosophical presuppositions as to how man began, one should view the evidence in its entirety. A careful comparison of travellers' accounts from various parts of the world and a selection only of those characteristics in living societies that could be found worldwide would guarantee, in Ferguson's view, a more valid view of how human culture and civilization arose.

It is not clear that Ferguson followed his own methodology. In any event, he posited that earliest man lived like the contemporary savages of his own time. Subsistence was by hunting, fishing and collecting wild plants. Hardly any form of government, religious system of belief, or personal property existed. (This picture was based mainly on writers' accounts of the American Indians.) Early man had no general principles of thought and little, if any, foresight. But even at this early stage man was susceptible of improvement, and his capacity for progress laid the groundwork for the next stage.

Improvements in the means of acquiring food and the establishment of private property led to barbarism. The barbarians domesticated animals and began to cultivate the soil. They followed leaders who rose to the top due to noble birth and wealth in private property. Unequal ownership of the land and commodities led to classes in society. Warfare increased, with the good points, in Ferguson's view, of developing fidelity, valour and solidarity.

Increasing occupational specialization led to a civil society. Special interest groups, the increased number of classes and a check and balance system eventually arose within society. Liberty was preserved due to a cultural tension between the several special interest groups in the society.

Perhaps the most extensive scheme to account for man's rise to civilization was that of Giambattista Vico, the Neapolitan Catholic philosopher. In the *Scienza nuova*, which went through three editions between 1725 and 1744, he sketched out the transitional stages which led to the development of civilization and culture. While his work was scarcely read in his own time it was to influence radically the later work of Barthold Georg Niebuhr and the German historical school in the nineteenth century, as well as Jules Michelet in France, who fundamentally altered French historiography.

Vico figures prominently in historians' accounts of the history of history. This is due to the fact that he reacted against the tendency of his contemporary philosophers and dilettantes to model history after the physical sciences. This cut at the roots of the Enlightenment philosophy, which maintained that one could establish hypotheses and natural laws to account for the origins and development of societies. As Carl Becker has succinctly stated, the goal of the seventeenth- and eighteenth-century philosophers was to bring the heavenly city of Augustine to earth by uncovering, and then assisting, the effect of natural laws. Besides the figures mentioned here we could add Condillac, Turgot and Condorcet in the eighteenth century, and names like Henri de Saint-Simon, August Comte, John Stuart Mill and Henry Thomas Buckle in the nineteenth. Vico was not the only person to react against the concept of natural laws operating in human societies. Joseph de Maistre, Arthur Schopenhauer, Johann Gottfried von Herder and Jacob Burckhardt also challenged such optimistic and rationalistic presuppositions as mere articles of Enlightenment faith. Karl Popper carried many of these same criticisms into the twentieth century by demonstrating that many of the high-sounding generalizations of historians of this bent fail to measure up to the conceptual precision and falsifiability of physical science models and theories.

Another notable contribution of Vico was to reason that in order truly to know something it was necessary to have made or fashioned it. He used this premise to argue that, if anything, history was superior to the physical sciences. This was due to the fact that the scientist was attempting to study the creation of God, which only God can properly know for certain. The 'world of nations', on the other hand, can be known, Vico argued, since it is the creation of man. The problem with this whole line of reasoning is a failure to recognize God's transcendence in history and the value of revelation. Vico was clearly correct in maintaining the essential 'otherness' of history as compared to the sciences.

While Vico recognized a providential principle immanent in the determinate stages through which societies pass, this was the same type of providence of the Enlightenment philosophers and far removed from that of the God of the Judeo-Christian heritage. Vico's philosophical bias can easily be shown by the first stage of his history of mankind. The earliest people were giants who lacked reason and were animists. Terrified of Jove (note the classical influence) who hurled thunderbolts, they lived in fear in caves. At first they shared women and possessions but finally were led to capture wives for themselves. The commonality of possessions led to quarrels, with the result that the strong killed the weak or caused them to flee to other strong protectors. Those fleeing to others led to the next stage where simple social structures beyond family ties became fixed.

Ultimately, a new culture arose, the Age of Heroes. Mars and Venus became the key religious symbols. Life no longer depended on the vicissitudes of Jove but now hinged on fate, which the gods controlled. Language originated during this stage, as nobles began to resort to speech after exhausting the possibilities of a visual communication system. These nobles followed a Spartan regime, treating wives as slaves, harshly punishing their children and playing strenuous games. These aristocrats then banded together into kingdoms where courts of justice were instituted.

Vico conceived of these stages as being cyclical in nature. Each stage was composed of three periods which were dominated respectively by the gods (religion), heroes (myth) and men (philosophy). While the dominance of religion, myth and philosophy in each stage succeeded one another in cycles, this 'diversity of modes' was always an upward-spiralling movement or evolution.

This overriding preoccupation with man's inevitable progress is not only apparent in all attempts to account for man's culture and civilization, but is obvious in most of the other historical writing of the period. Gibbon's animosity towards Christianity is well known. Less well known are Gibbon's reasons for writing a *History of the Decline and Fall of the Roman Empire*. The primary concern of this masterpiece of philosophical history was to demonstrate that the Europe of

Gibbon's own day had attained a superior degree of development that made it immune to the fate of the ancient world. His
criticisms against Christianity in the empire were influenced
by his rejection of supernaturalism, not the historical documents he consulted. Man's progress was seen as the result of a
totally natural process. God's intervention or transcendence
in history was viewed as an impossibility. Nature had been
enthroned as god, and natural law would run its course with
man the supreme beneficiary (Manuel).

One other towering figure of the Enlightenment must be
mentioned, Antoine Nicolas de Condorcet. His *Esquisse d'un
tableau historique des progrès de l'esprit humain,* published in 1794,
set out ten stages of a 'hypothetical history of a single people'
by selectively choosing events from the histories of various
peoples and combining them in an evolutionary progression.
Briefly stated, the stages proceed as follows: (1) hunting and
fishing (appearance of the family and human language); (2)
pastoral (beginning of private property); (3) from settled
agriculture to the appearance of alphabetical writing (government first appears); (4) Greece (flowering of art and
philosophy); (5) Rome (fuller development of law and
government); (6) early Middle Ages; (7) late Middle Ages; (8)
from the invention of printing to Descartes; (9) from Descartes
to the revolution of 1789; and (10) the post 1789-period.
Condorcet's purpose was to show that the French people were
the end result of such progression and would surely go on to
lead the world to further development.

Condorcet, like many of the other writers we have
mentioned during this period, reacted against the standard
historical writing of his day, which consisted of chronicles of
events. He was concerned once again to formulate general
laws that would be true for all nations at all times. His
concern was not so much with what had happened but with
what inevitably must occur. Thus he argues that printing,
based on the alphabet, had brought about an intellectual
climate where judgements could be formed independently of
tradition and these judgements would undermine traditional
(and tyrannical) authority of both church and state.

The nineteenth century

By the time we reach Darwin's century there is clearly already an often used evolutionary framework to explain man's culture and civilization. Its origins can be traced back to ancient times and it existed quite independently of any theory of biological evolution. It is for this reason that perceptive historians of man's ideas about culture and society have argued for some time that Darwin's impact in the social sciences, and certainly history in particular, has been far overstated by exponents of Darwinism or neo-Darwinian philosophy (Bock, Bowler, Collingwood, Greene, Voget, White).

Within Darwin's lifetime figures like Maine, Marx, Engels and Lewis Henry Morgan formulated evolutionary explanations for man's culture and civilization with no obvious links to Darwinian biology. Marx's and Engels' formulation of man's cultural development was explicitly stated in *The German Ideology* (written from 1845-46) and in Marx's *A Contribution to Political Economy*, published in the same year as Darwin's *Origin* (Mandelbaum). Evolutionary in nature, their scheme envisaged five stages in man's cultural development.

1. 'Asiatic' type, where there are small, isolated, egalitarian village communities. All land belongs to the monarch and is worked by villagers who receive little in return. Tradition rigorously governs behaviour.

2. Ancient society, which is based on the city-state. This stage is marked by greater individualism, a division of labour and trade and class boundaries. Conflicts surface from time to time between powerful landowners and lowly slaves.

3. Feudal society, where self-sufficient peasants work land owned by feudal lords.

4. Capitalism, where the means of production are freely available and labour can move wherever conditions are best. Most goods are intended for the market and division of labour and trade grows enormously.

5. Socialism.

The intellectual link between Marx and Darwin is by no means settled historiographically but it appears that Darwin's influence on Marx was minimal, as recent papers by Feuer,

Fay, Carroll, Berlin and Colp and Fay indicate. Zavadskii has
been the only one to my knowledge who has probed the
relationship between Engels and Darwin.

Lewis Henry Morgan, whose book *Ancient Society* delighted
Marx and Engels, envisaged three stages with three periods
for the two lower stages. His scheme can be set out as follows:

Stage 1 — Savagery
    Period 1 — Lower savagery (infancy of human species,
                  no real progress of any sort).
    Period 2 — Middle savagery (culminating in the ac-
                  quisition of fire).
    Period 3 — Upper savagery (invention of the bow).

Stage 2 — Barbarism
    Period 1 — Invention of pottery and in the Western
                  hemisphere, horticulture.
    Period 2 — Middle barbarism (animal domestication
                  in the Eastern hemisphere).
    Period 3 — Upper barbarism (use of iron tools in Old
                  World).

Stage 3 — Civilization (use of the phonetic alphabet).

Each period is a step up in technological progress and
possesses its own particular forms of marriage, family and
other social structures which Morgan happily outlined for his
reader. Logical processes that were innate in the human mind
prompted further improvements. This meant that although
there are definite differences in man's progress on all
continents, overall there is relative uniformity. Cultural
development occurred by an unconscious selection of progressive traits that enables the individuals of that society to solve a
new problem or alleviate pressing needs (cultural adaptation).
Cultural conditions limit what will be adopted, while at the
same time serving to highlight the value of new traits for
continued adaptation.

Herbert Spencer, in formulating his evolutionary ideas of
social origins and development, also does not appear to have
been influenced by Darwinism, despite many claims in
standard texts to the contrary (Carneiro, Bock and Leeds in

Glick). His evolutionism was non-linear and seems to have been most influenced by the embryological researches and speculations of Von Baer. Finally, we may note that the standard three-age system (Stone, Bronze and Iron) used to this day in archaeology and prehistory, originated with Christian J. Thomsen, who used this framework to display artefacts in the Danish National Museum from 1819 onwards (Stoltman). This concept, while evolutionary in nature, was also not derived from biological evolutionism.

The twentieth century

While it would be impossible effectively to outline develop-ments in the twentieth century within the scope of this paper, I believe that my thesis holds. If one reads carefully the writings of Edward B. Taylor, Vere Gordon Childe, Leslie A. White, Julian H. Steward, Elman R. Service and Robert Redfield, to name a few, it becomes abundantly clear that cultural evolution is not influenced heavily (if at all) by biological theorizing, but exists independently of, albeit complementary to, evolutionary explanations of the natural world at large (Harris, Honigmann, Murphee).

It should be noted that, to this day, ideas abound in the fields of archaeology, prehistory and history, concerning how man derived his culture and civilization. Recent research in the origins of agriculture indicate the presence of many competing models and scenarios but no consensus (Reed). Broader questions as to the origins of civilization itself also admit of no easy solutions in the evolutionary camp at present (Moorey). It does appear that the ancient Near East is still the area of the world where civilization first emerged. This is assuming that the presence of cities is a valid indicator of the emergence of civilization! Information available from these disciplines appears to tie in well with the diffusionism we see in the early chapters of Genesis after the Flood. Continuing research in the Levant and Egypt keeps pushing back the time scale of evolutionary explanations but has not succeeded in demonstrating a viable, concrete picture of the emergence of culture (Bar-Yosef, Burney, Finegan, Lloyd, Oates, Sherratt).

Research into the Palaeolithic and Mesolithic in recent

years has made it clear that even at this 'stage' (I suspect geographical locality and not age is the main factor here) man has evidence of intellectual, social and technological capacities (Marshack, Moore, Smith). Studies of spatial organization suggest that often differing needs and supplies affected tool use and type, and that these industries often functioned co-terminously with other radically different types of industries for certain time periods (Hodder). The transition from bronze to iron is now known to be due not so much to desirable qualities in the respective metals, but to problems of the supply of raw materials (Maddin, Muhly and Wheeler). Whether archaeology can succeed, in the near future, in providing a reliable reconstruction of man's cultural past is open to severe question. Professional archaeologists are in no more agreement now as to acceptable methodologies and theoretical orientation than they were fifteen years ago (cf. Trigger with comments following Read and LeBlanc). The present concern with theoretical formulations and a greater willingness to acknowledge presuppositions has led to an overturning of some previously accepted ideas concerning man's cultural development, as a recent work on primitive religions demonstrates (Evans-Pritchard).

Evolutionism is still alive but not well in historical writing. In part this is due to the fact that history is concerned with unique events. The search for general laws of historical explanation has been given up, after courageous attempts by the likes of Oswald Spengler, Arnold J. Toynbee, Jacques Pirenne and Eric Vogel to maintain their viability. The history of history clearly demonstrates a much stronger influence of evolutionism in the past as a powerful philosophical presupposition in historical writing than in the present. This influence goes back to antiquity and existed independently of biological evolutionary theories. As a result of its escape from evolutionism, historical writing today is in a healthier position even though other naturalistic presuppositions still play an important role in shaping (and inevitably biasing) much that is written. Evolutionism survives in historical language only in the broad meaning of 'change'. It is, of course, clear that this type of 'evolution' does exist in the history of human societies and civilization.

Someone writing history with supernaturalistic presuppositions will view history in a different, albeit equally biased, light. This can be seen in comparing a recent work on the history of Christianity with standard texts in the field (Briggs, *et. al.*). Recently produced secondary school texts by Robert Clouse, Gerard Pierard and Mary Stanton show how such biblically centred presuppositions affect the handling of the historical narrative of Western civilization.

Bibliography

Many of the ideas expressed in this paper have been formed over a considerable length of time. Works that have been influential in affecting my own thinking as well as specific works mentioned in the text are listed here for future reference.

Albright, William Foxwell. *The Biblical Period from Abraham to Ezra: A Historical Survey*, Harper and Row Inc., New York, 1963.
  History, Archaeology, and Christian Humanism, Adam and Charles Black, London, 1964.
  From the Stone Age to Christianity — Monotheism and the Historical Process, Doubleday and Co., Garden City, New York, 1957.
Auerbach, Erich. *Mimesis: The Representation of Reality in Western Literature*, trans. Willard Trask, Princeton University Press, Princeton, 1968.
Augustine. *City of God*, trans. and ed. by Vernon J. Bourke, Doubleday and Co., Garden City, New York, 1958.
Bar-Yosef, O. 'Prehistory of the Levant', *Annual Review of Anthropology*, 9: 101-160, 1980.
Becker, Carl. *The Heavenly City of the Eighteenth Century Philosophers*, Yale University Press, New Haven, 1960.
Berlin, Isaiah. 'Marx's Kapital and Darwin', *Journal of the History of Ideas*, 39: 519, 1978.
Bock, Kenneth E. 'Darwin and Social Theory', *Philosophy of Science*, 22: 123-134, 1955.
  'Theories of Progress, Development, and Evolution', *A History of Sociological Analysis*, Eds. Tom Bottomore, Robert Nisbet, Heinemann. London, 1978, pp. 39-79.
Boemus, Johann. *The Fardle of Facions Conteining the Aunciente Maners, Custumes, and Lawes of the Peoples Enhabiting the two Partes of the Earthe Called Africke and Asia*, trans. William M. Waterman, E. and G. Goldsmid Pub., London, 3 vols., 1888.

Bowler, Peter J. 'Evolutionism in the Enlightenment', *History of Science*, 12: 159-183, 1974.

Briggs, John *et. al. The Lion Handbook to the History of Christianity*, Lion Publishing, Tring, Herts, 1982.

Bright, John. *A History of Israel*, Westminster Press, Phila., 3rd ed., 1981.

Bruce, F.F. *Israel and the Nations: From the Exodus to the Fall of the Second Temple*, Eerdmans Pub., Grand Rapids, 1963.

New Testament History, Doubleday and Co., Garden City, New York, 1969.

Burckhardt, Jacob. *Force and Freedom: An Interpretation of History*, Ed. James H. Nichols, Meridian Books, New York, 1955.

Burney, Charles. *From Village to Empire — An Introduction to Near Eastern Archaeology*, Phaidon Press, Oxford, 1977.

Bury, J.B. *The Idea of Progress — An Inquiry into its Origin and Growth*, Greenwood Press Pub., Westport, Conn., 1982 (reprint of 1932 Macmillan ed.).

Butterfield, Herbert. *Christianity and History*, G. Bell and Sons Ltd., London, 1950.

'Historiography', *Dictionary of the History of Ideas*, Ed. Philip P. Wiener, Charles Scribner's Sons, New York, 1973, 2: 464-498.

The Origins of History, Basic Books, New York, 1981.

Cairns, Earle E. *God and Man in Time — A Christian Approach to Historiography*, Baker Book House, Grand Rapids, 1979.

Campbell, Edward F., Robert G. Boling, Eds. *Essays in Honour of George Ernest Wright*, Scholars Press, Missoula, Montana, 1976.

J. Maxwell Miller. 'W.F. Albright and Historical Reconstruction', *Biblical Archaeologist*, 42(1): 37-48, 1979.

Carneiro, Robert L. 'Structure, Function, and Equilibrium in the Evolutionism of Herbert Spencer', *Journal of Anthropological Research*, 29: 77-95, 1973.

Carroll, P.T. 'Correction to Margaret A. Fay's Article', *Journal of the History of Ideas*, 39: 675-676, 1978.

Childe, Vere Gordon. *Man Makes Himself*, New American Library, New York, 1951.

Social Evolution, Watts and Co., London, 1951.

Collingwood, Robin G. *The Idea of History*, Oxford University Press, Oxford, 1946.

Colp, Ralph Jr. 'The contacts between Karl Marx and Charles Darwin', *Journal of the History of Ideas*, 35: 329-338, 1974.

Margaret A. Fay. 'Independent Scientific Discoveries and the Darwin-Marx letter', *Journal of the History of Ideas*, 40: 479, 1979.

Condorcet, Antoine Nicolas de. *Sketch for a Historical Picture of the Progress of the Human Mind*, trans. June Barraclough, Noonday Press, New York, 1955.

Croce, Benedetto. *History: Its Theory and Method*, trans. Douglas Ainslee, Harcourt, Brace, Co., New York, 1923.

Custance, Arthur C. 'Flood Traditions of the World', *A Symposium on Creation IV*, Donald W. Patten, *et. al.*, Baker Book House, Grand Rapids, 1972, 9-44.

   The Doorway Papers, reprinted in 10 volumes, Zondervan Pub., Grand Rapids, 1968-1980.

DeVaux, Roland. *The Early History of Israel: To the Period of the Judges*, Westminster Press. Phila., 1976.

Dooyeweerd, Herman. *In the Twilight of Western Thought*, Craig Press, Nutley, N.J., 1975.

Dray, William H. Ed. *Philosophical Analysis and History*, Harper and Row, New York, 1966.

Evans-Prichard, E.E. *Theories of Primitive Religion*, Clarendon Press, Oxford, 1965.

Ferguson, Adam. *An Essay on the History of Civil Society*, Ed. Duncan Forbes, Edinburgh Univ. Press, Edin., 1966.

Fay, Margaret A. 'Did Marx offer to dedicate Capital to Darwin?', a reassessment', *Journal of the History of Ideas*, 39: 133-146, 1978.

Forster, Roger T. V. Paul Marston. *God's Strategy in Human History*, Send the Light Trust, Bromley, Kent, 1973.

Feuer, L.S. 'Is the Darwin-Marx correspondence authentic?', *Annals of Science*, 32: 1-12, 1975.

Gardiner, Patrick, Ed. *Theories of History*, The Free Press, New York, 1959.

Gilkey, Lagdon. *Reaping the Whirlwind — A Christian Interpretation of History*, Seabury Press, New York, 1976.

Glass, Bentley, Owsei Temkin, William L. Straus Jr., Eds, *Forerunners of Darwin, 1745-1859*, The Johns Hopkins Univ. Press, Balto., 1968.

Glick, Thomas F. Ed. *The Comparative Reception of Darwinism*, Univ. of Texas Press, Austin, 1974.

Greene, John c. *The Death of Adam: Evolution and Its Impact on Western Thought*, Iowa State Univ. Press, Ames, 1959.

Griffiths, J.G. 'Archaeology and Hesiod's Five Ages', *Journal of the History of Ideas*, 17: 109-119, 1956.

Harris, Marvin. *The Rise of Anthropological Theory: A History of Theories of Culture*, Thomas Y. Cromwell Co., New York, 1968.

Hayes, John J., J. Maxwell Miller, Eds. *Israelite and Judean History*, The Westminster Press, Phila., 1977.

Hegel, Georg W. Friedrich. *The Philosophy of History*, trans. J. Sibree, Dover Pub., New York, 1956.

Herder, Johann Gottfried. *Reflections on the Philosophy of History of Mankind*, trans. T.O. Churchill, Ed. Frank E. Manuel, Univ. of Chicago Press, Chicago, 1966.

Hermann, Seigfried. *A History of Israel in Old Testament Times*, Fortress Press, Phila., 1975.

Holt, P.M., Ann K.S. Lambton, Bernard Lewis, Eds. *The Cambridge History of Islam*, Cambridge Univ. Press, Cambridge, London, 1970, Vol. 2B.

Home, Henry. *Sketches of the History of Man*, George Olms Verlags-buchhandlung, Hildesheim, 4 vols, 1968.

Honigmann, John J. *The Development of Anthropological Ideas*, The Dorsey Press, Homewood, Ill., 1976.

Hooykaas, Reijer. *Religion and the Rise of Modern Science*, Scottish Academic Press, Edinburgh, 1972.

Imerti, Arthur D. Ed. *The Expulsion of the Triumphant Beast*, by Giordano Bruno, Rutger's Univ. Press, New Brunswick, N.J., 1964.

Ives, E.W. *God in History*, Lion Pub., Tring, Herts, 1979.

Jaki, Stanley L. *The Road of Science and the Ways to God*, Univ. of Chicago Press, Chicago, 1978.

Science and Creation — From Eternal Cycles to an Oscillating Universe, Scottish Academic Press, Edinburgh, 1974.

Josephus. *Complete Works*, trans. William Whiston, Kregel Pub., Grand Rapids, 1981.

Kant, Immanuel. *On History*, ed. Lewis White Beck, Bobbs-Merrill Co., New York, 1963.

Khaldûn, Ibn. *An Introduction to History — the Mugaddimah*, trans. Franz Rosenthal, ed. N.J. Dawood, Routledge and Kegan Paul, London, 1967.

Klaaren, Eugene M. *Religious Origins of Modern Science — Belief in Creation in Seventeenth Century Thought*, William B. Eerdmans Pub., Grand Rapids, 1977.

Kroebner, A.L. Clyde Kluckholn. *Culture*, Harvard University Press, Cambridge, Mass., 1952.

LeGoff, Jacques, Roger Chartier, Jacques Revel. *La Nouvelle Histoire*, C.E.P.L., Paris, 1978.

Lee, Francis Nigel. *Communist Eschatology — A Christian Philosophical Analysis of the Post-Capitalistic Views of Marx, Engels, and Lenin*, Craig Press, Nutley, N.J., 1974.

Leff, Gordon. *History and Social Theory*, Doubleday-Anchor Books, Garden City, New York, 1971.

Lewis, Clive Staples. *Christian Reflections*, Ed. Walter Hooper, William B. Eerdmans Pub., Grand Rapids, 1967.

Lloyd, Seton. *The Archaeology of Mesopotamia*, Thames and Hudson, London, 1978.

Lods, Adolphe. *Isräel — Des origines au milieu du VIIIᵉ siècle avant notre ère*, Editions Albin Michel, Paris, 1969.

Lutz, Henry F. 'The Sumerians and Anthropology', *American Anthropologist*, 29: 202-209, 1927.

Maddin, Robert, James D. Muhly, Tamara S. Wheeler. 'How the Iron Age Began', *Scientific American*, 237 (4): 122-131, 1977.

Manuel, Frank E. *The Eighteenth Century Confronts the Gods*, Harvard University Press, Cambridge, Mass., 1959.

Mandelbaum, Maurice. *History, Man, and Reason*, The Johns Hopkins University Press, Balto., 1971.

Marshack, Alexander. *The Roots of Civilization*, McGraw-Hill Book Co., New York, 1972.

McCone, Clyde R. 'The Origins of Civilization: Archaeological Data and Problems of Evolutionary Explanation', *A Symposium on Creation IV*, Donald W. Patten, *et. al.*, Baker Book House, Grand Rapids, 1972, pp. 123-133.

'The Origins of Civilization', *A Symposium on Creation*, Henry Morris, *et. al.*, Baker Book House, Grand Rapids, 1968, pp. 81-92.

'Evolutionary Time: A Moral Issue', *A Symposium on Creation*, Henry Morris, *et. al.*, Baker Book House, Grand Rapids, 1968, pp. 139-155.

'Genesis time: A Spiritual Consideration', *A Symposium on Creation II*, Donald W. Patten, *et. al.*, Baker Book House, Grand Rapids, 1970, pp. 105-116.

Meyers, Eric M. 'The Bible and Archaeology', *The Biblical Archaeologist*, 47(1): 36-40, 1984.

Michelet, Jules. *Introduction à l'histoire universelle, tableau de la France, préface de 1869*, Cluny, Paris, 1961.

Miller, J. Maxwell. 'Approaches to the Bible Through History and Archaeology: Biblical History as a Discipline', *The Biblical Archaeologist*, 45(4): 211-216, 1982.

Momigliano, Arnaldo. 'Biblical Studies and Classical Studies: Simple Reflections about Historical Method', *The Biblical Archaeologist*, 45(4): 224-228, 1982.

Montgomery, John Warwick. *The Shape of the Past — A Christian Response to Secular Philosophies of History*, Bethany Fellowship Inc., Minneapolis, 2nd ed., 1975.

Where is History Going? — A Christian Response to Secular Philosophies of History, Bethany Fellowship Inc., Minneapolis, 1969.

Moore, Andrew M.T. 'A Pre-Neolithic Farmers' Village on the Euphrates', *Scientific American*, 241(2): 62-70, 1979.

Moorey, P.R.S. Ed. *The Origins of Civilization*, Clarendon Press, Oxford, 1979.

Morgan, Lewis Henry. *Ancient Society*, Ed. Leslie A. White, Belknap Press of Harvard University, Cambridge, Mass., 1964.

Murphee, I.L. 'The Evolutionary Anthropologists: The Concept of Progress and Culture in the Thought of John Lubbock, Edward B. Taylor, and Lewis H. Morgan', *American Philosophical Society Proceedings*, 101: 265-300, 1961.

Noth, Martin. *A History of the Pentateuchal Traditions*, Prentice-Hall Pub., Englewood Cliffs, N.J., 1972.

The History of Israel, Harper and Row, New York, 2nd ed., 1960.

Oates, Joan. *Babylon*, Thames and Hudson, London, 1979.

Peardon, Thomas P. Ed. *The Second Treatise of Government by John Locke*, Bobbs-Merrill Co., Indianapolis, 1952.

Pollard, Sydney. *The Idea of Progress*, Watts and Co., London, 1968

Popper, Karl, R. *The Poverty of Historicism*, Routledge and Kegan Paul, London, 1961.

Ranke, Leopald Von. *The Theory and Practice of History*, trans. Wilma A. Iggers, Konrad von Moltke, Ed. Georg G. Iggers, Konrad von Moltke, Bobbs-Merrill Co., New York, 1973.

Read, Dwight W., Steven A. LeBlanc. 'Descriptive Statements, Covering Laws, and Theories in Archaeology', *Current Anthropology*, 19(2): 307-335, 1978.

Reed, Charles A. *The Origin of Agriculture*, Mouton Press, The Hague, 1977.

Robinson, John M. *An Introduction to Greek Philosophy*, Houghton Mifflin Co., Boston, 1968.

Russell, C.A. Ed. *Science and Religious Belief — A Selection of Recent Historical Studies*, University of London Press, London, 1973.

Serejski, M.H. 'Charles Darwin's Views on History', *Scientia*, 105: 757-761, 1970.

Sherratt, Andrew, Ed. *The Cambridge Encyclopedia of Archaeology*, Cambridge University Press, New York, 1980.

Smith, Philip E.L. 'Stone Age Man on the Nile', *Scientific American*, 235(2): 30-38, 1976.

Speiser, Ephraim. *The Anchor Bible-Genesis*, Anchor Doubleday Co., Garden City, New York, 1964.

Stoltman, James B. 'Temporal Models in Prehistory: An Example from Eastern North America', *Current Anthropology*, 19(4): 703-746, 1978.

Toynbee, Arnold. *A Study of History*, Oxford University Press, London, 12 vols, 1934-61.

Trigger, Bruce G. 'Aims in Prehistoric Archaeology', *Antiquity*, 44: 26-37, 1970.

Vico, Giambattista. *The New Science*, trans. of third ed. of 1744 by Thomas G. Bergin, Max H. Fisch, Cornell Univ. Press, Ithaca, New York, 1968.

Vives, Juan Luis. *On Education: A Translation of the De Tradensis Disciplinis (1531)*, trans, and ed. Foster Watson, Cambridge Univ. Press, Cambridge, 1913.

Voget, Fred W. 'Progress, Science, History, and Evolution in Eighteenth and Nineteenth Century Anthropology', *Journal of the History of the Behavioural Sciences*, 3: 132-155, 1967.

White, Hayden. *Metahistory — The Historical Imagination in Nineteenth Century Europe*, The Johns Hopkins Univ. Press, Balto., 1973.

Wood, Leon T. *Survey of Israel's History*, Zondervan Pub., Grand Rapids, 1970.

Zavadskii, K.M., A.B. Georgievskii, A.P. Mozelov. 'Engels and Darwin', *Soviet Studies in Philosophy*, 10: 63-80, 1971.

6.

Human origins and the Olduvai finds

Gerald H. Duffett

Introduction

Anyone studying the state of palaeoanthropology in Africa will know that little sense is being made of hominid fossils. This short study tries to summarize the trends in classifying species as well as to highlight the many mistakes over fragmentary specimens and alleged tools that are nothing of the sort. It also tries to understand why Dr L.S.B. Leakey has gone against the view of most experts and split up some taxons while lumping others together. An attempt has been made to place the Olduvai Gorge fossils and excavations within the context of the quest for an African ancestor for Adam. Furthermore, the paper could serve as a sobering commentary on the following statement by Karl Pearson: 'Science consists not in absolute knowledge, but in the statement of the probable on the basis of our present — invariably limited — acquaintance with facts' (Campbell 1978, p.204).

1. Chosen site

Before considering why Dr Louis S.B. Leakey and his wife Mary D. Leakey chose to look for alleged human ancestors ('hominids') in the Olduvai Gorge and in other East African sites, we must first answer another question which is more general and fundamental. It is why Africa should be reckoned to have any relevance in the quest for early man.

Asia was — and to creationists still is — the most obvious choice for the location of the 'cradle of mankind'. Not only is the land mass of Asia the largest continent on present-day earth, but it is territory where interesting fossilized human remains have been discovered. Furthermore, and irrespective of any palaeoanthropological evidence, the rivers mentioned as being close to the site of the Garden of Eden are geographically identifiable entities within modern Asia.

The underlying reason why many scientists have scoured Africa for traces of ancient human life and for fossilized hominids is surely to do with Charles Darwin. It was he who suggested that Africa probably witnessed the appearance of man.

The explanation for Darwin's choice of Africa, the second largest of the present-day continents, would seem to lie in his fascination with chimpanzees. He reasoned that if mankind and the apes sprang from a common ancestor, then since chimpanzees and gorillas occur in Africa, 'ape-men' and early men must also have lived there.

Sir Arthur Keith has certainly shown that man shares more of his anatomical characteristics with the gorilla and the chimpanzee than with the orang-utan (von Koenigswald 1976, p.34). Therefore, as the first two mentioned apes occur in Africa and the third only lives wild on the islands of Borneo and Sumatra (which were once joined to the mainland of south-east Asia), then Africa seems a better choice than Asia. The reason for hoping to find 'connecting species' or 'link species' in Africa thus arises from comparative anatomy and primate zoogeography rather than some special insight on Darwin's part. Such transitional forms must, of course, remain purely hypothetical until found. That is why common ancestors are often referred to as 'missing links'.

Now let us return to the original question of why Dr and Mrs Leakey searched for hominids in East Africa and along the Olduvai Gorge in particular (see Fig. 1). Firstly, the sight of great depths of exposed sedimentary beds presents a challenge to any palaeontologist to excavate its fossil content. Secondly, attention was focused upon the Olduvai Gorge in 1913 when a German anthropologist found an intact human

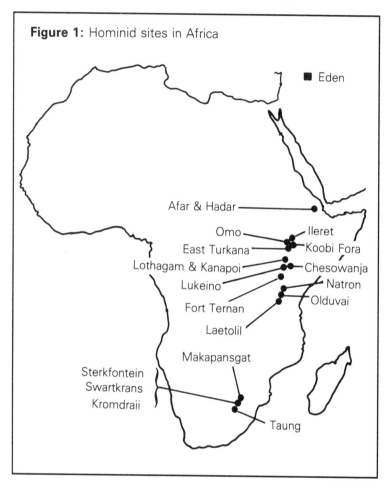

Figure 1: Hominid sites in Africa

- Eden
- Afar & Hadar
- Omo
- Ileret
- East Turkana
- Koobi Fora
- Lothagam & Kanapoi
- Chesowanja
- Lukeino
- Natron
- Fort Ternan
- Olduvai
- Laetolil
- Makapansgat
- Sterkfontein
- Swartkrans
- Kromdraii
- Taung

skeleton apparently associated with animal remains from the Pleistocene system. The alleged discovery of man in the Pleistocene did not convince evolutionists, but it was sufficient to whet their appetite. They hoped to find 'ape-men' in the Pliocene strata, or, better still from their point of view, in the underlying Miocene strata. So Dr Leakey and his wife set to work on the Olduvai Gorge in 1931 (Campbell 1978, p.132).

2. Considerable stamina

Soon after the Leakeys started their excavations at Olduvai, they discovered a problem for the human skeleton found by Hans Reck in 1913. It was proved to have been an intrusive burial from a much higher level than the Pleistocene with its fossils and stone tools. Therefore that specimen, at least, was no longer associated with the Pleistocene (Campbell 1978, p.132). But the Leakeys persevered. They wanted to find the remains of the real being that had shaped those Pleistocene tools.

In 1935 Dr Leakey found two parietal bone fragments that were identified as hominid. They came from either Bed III or Bed IV (shown in Fig. 2, based on Oakley & Campbell 1977, p.167) at site MNK within the Olduvai Gorge (see Fig. 3, based on Oakley & Campbell 1977, p.169). Then, twenty years later, he discovered two teeth from the milk set of an infant, which could also have been regarded as a hominid. The specimens consisted of a deciduous canine and a deciduous molar. Both came from Bed II (shown in Fig. 2) and from site BK within the Olduvai Gorge (see Fig. 3).

Although the evidence for hominids amounted to only two bones and a couple of teeth, which seems a poor return for twenty-four years in the scorching heat of the African sun, the Leakey couple did not end their hunt for the so-called 'missing link'. It is intriguing to try to understand what maintained their efforts.

One commendable factor was their mutual interest. Not only did Mary Leakey help raise her family, she also did the lion's share in the on-site excavations while her husband was engaged in his work as Director of the Coryndon Museum (which was the forerunner of the Kenya National Museum) and also in public lectures in many parts of the world.

Another factor was the news from time to time of fresh discoveries elsewhere of apparently ancient human remains with skulls showing features no longer common in living populations. Also the discovery of australopithecine remains in South Africa must have kept alive the hope that some extinct apes would be found further north in Kenya and perhaps prove to be the long-expected hominids (see Fig. 1). Perhaps the African rift-valleys not far from Olduvai

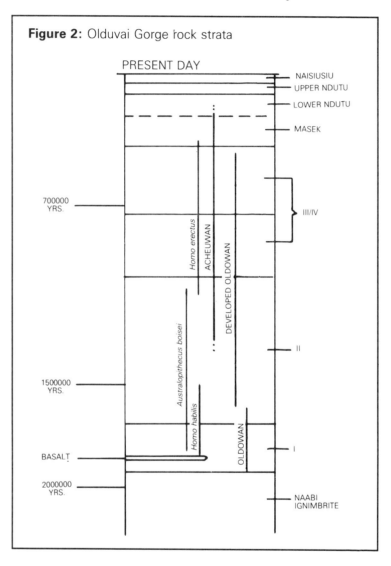

Figure 2: Olduvai Gorge rock strata

Gorge and other sites of excavation might contain specimens of evolving hominids migrating either southwards to Rhodesia and South Africa or northwards to the Middle East.

Then things started to happen in 1959. Mary Leakey found an *Australopithecus*-like skull in Bed I of the Olduvai Gorge.

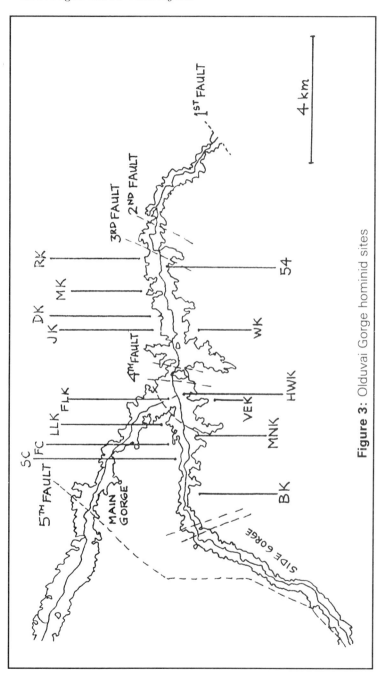

Figure 3: Olduvai Gorge hominid sites

Promptly she and her husband drew attention to features that they reckoned made their find more human than specimens found previously in South Africa. But their excitement over the discovery of their so-called 'Nutcracker Man' (alias 'East African Man'), whose scientific name is *Zinjanthropus boisei*, was short-lived (see Fig. 4).

In 1960, the very next year, another specimen was found. It belonged to a different species and was given the name *Homo habilis*, meaning 'Handy Man'. But what was tantalizing about this, more human, species was that it came from a deeper level in Bed I than the horizon where *Zinjanthropus boisei* was found (Wood 1978, p.41).

If in 1959 the Leakeys thought they had found the proverbial crock of gold, in 1960 they dug deeper and found the proverbial Pandora's box. What is more, they opened it and reported their find to the scientific world.

3. Controversial statements

Cases are known where an expert palaeontologist overpraises the significance of a particular fossil specimen, especially one which he or she has personally excavated and reported to the scientific community. Often the exaggerated claim is that the fossil is closer than similar specimens to being a so-called 'link species'. As such, it would be of greater ancestor-descendant significance than the rest.

Of course, any misguided evolutionary phylogeny would soon be refuted by rival palaeontologists. They would accuse their colleague of 'discoverer's bias', a condition epitomized by the Argentinian palaeontologist Carlo Ameghino. He believed that the fossils he found were the direct ancestors of present-day animals or modern men, whereas those found by other workers represented only unimportant side-branches that led to extinction. That episode gave rise to the term 'Ameghino Complex' (Simons 1972, p.52).

When Leakey conferred the generic name *Zinjanthropus* upon his wife's 1959 discovery he was suffering from a touch of the 'Ameghino Complex'. How else can anyone account for the criticisms uttered by his fellow evolutionists? Regarding that 1959 specimen (which was originally given Reg. no. AH/

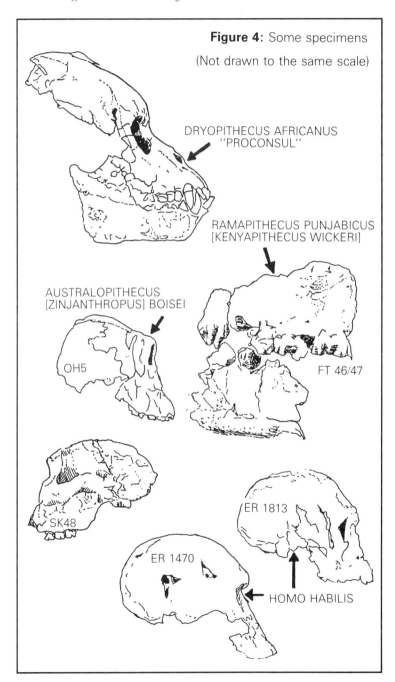

Figure 4: Some specimens
(Not drawn to the same scale)

DRYOPITHECUS AFRICANUS
"PROCONSUL"

RAMAPITHECUS PUNJABICUS
[KENYAPITHECUS WICKERI]

AUSTRALOPITHECUS
[ZINJANTHROPUS] BOISEI

OH5

FT 46/47

SK48

ER 1813

ER 1470

HOMO HABILIS

65.1 and has since been catalogued as OH 5) von Koenigswald stated: 'It is considered an australopithecine by all who
have inspected the find' (von Koenigswald 1976, p.70).
Similarly, but with a hesitancy that savours of gentle
diplomacy, Bernard G. Campbell declared: 'It is probably
true to say that most authorities have now agreed that a
convincing case has not yet been made out for separating
these fossils generically' (Campbell 1987, p.22). In other
words, specimen OH 5 really belongs to the genus *Ausralopithe-*
cus ('Southern Ape') and it was a mistake on Leakey's part to
have called it *Zinjanthropus*. Therefore OH 5 should nowadays
be regarded as the remains of an extinct form of ape. In the
estimation of evolutionists OH 5 is neither 'Nutcracker Man'
nor 'East Africa Man'.

But changing the generic name of OH 5 from *Zinjanthropus*
to *Australopithecus* does not alter the fact that its remains were
found associated with stone artefacts. The answer to the
problem of the tools was discovered in 1960 when parts of a
skull and the remains of a hand (minus the thumb!) were
found at about the same level in Bed I of the Olduvai Gorge
and close to where OH 5 had been found. The new specimen
was catalogued as OH 7 and the remains of a foot closely
associated with it as OH 8 (Campbell 1978, p.125). Both
specimens pointed to a being more human than *Zinjanthropus*
existing at about the same time (but see section 5 of this
paper). So Dr Leakey then came to believe that the species
represented by remains such as OH 7 and OH 8 was the real
maker of the tools he had mistakenly attributed to OH 5
(Wood 1978, p.41).

At first OH 7 was called 'pre-*Zinj*' (Simons 1972, p.277).
From a geological point of view specimens of the same type
have since been found at lower levels in Bed I and so there is
no doubt that a more human type of being existed earlier than
OH 5. Then in 1964 along with other authorities Leakey
renamed 'pre-*Zinj*' as *Homo habilis* and controversy continues
to rage!

It is ironical that Dr Leakey helped to show that Reck's
intact skeleton was not really connected with the stone tools
around it and yet managed to fall into the same trap over the
1959 discovery of OH 5 close to a 'living floor' containing
stone artefacts, waste flakes and butchered animal bones. In

each case the error was to assume that an association of excavated materials implied a relationship of attribution. Bones of the butchered animals did not belong to the maker of the stone tools. In both instances cited in this paragraph the stones in question were older than their alleged shapers (i.e. toolmakers) and thus had no connection with them.

Incidentally, many cases are known where bones of two species have been intermingled or found closely associated and the result has been to reconstruct an erroneous 'hybrid' species. For example, it is uncertain whether the toothed jaws belong to the rest of the skeleton of the Cretaceous bird named *Ichthyornis*. It seems more likely that they belong instead to a 'baby' mosasaur, which is a type of marine lizard (Romer 1966, pp.171-2).

No review of controversial statements about man's alleged origin would be complete unless some reference was made to two species found away from the Olduvai Gorge. Both specimens were found within the so-called Miocene deposits of Kenya. One was discovered by Mary Leakey at Rusinga Island, Lake Victoria and was named 'Proconsul' after a newly-born ape in London's Regents Park Zoo in 1948. The other was found by Heslon Mukiri, a foreman of the 1960 Leakey expedition at Fort Ternan. As it was given the generic name of *Kenyapithecus* after the country in which it was found, it would have seemed fitting for it to have received the specific epithet of *mukiri* after its discoverer, but instead it was called *K. wickeri* (see figure 4; Simons 1972, p.187).

Dr Leakey examined the almost complete skull of the 'Proconsul' specimen and declared it to be related to man (*Homo sapiens*) on the grounds that it had neither browridges nor a 'simian shelf' across the gap behind the front of its lower jaw (von Koenigswald 1976, pp.58-59). As so-called 'modern' man lacks both features, which are possessed by large anthropoid apes such as the chimpanzee and gorilla, Dr Leakey would seem to have a point. However, Milford Wolpoff reckons that individual features such as the brow-ridges can change and 'reverse'. Therefore, he argues, such features cannot be used to decide which fossils may or may not be human ancestors (Wolpoff 1980, p.34).

But what about the lower jaw structure of 'Proconsul', which Leakey cited as evidence for its being a remote

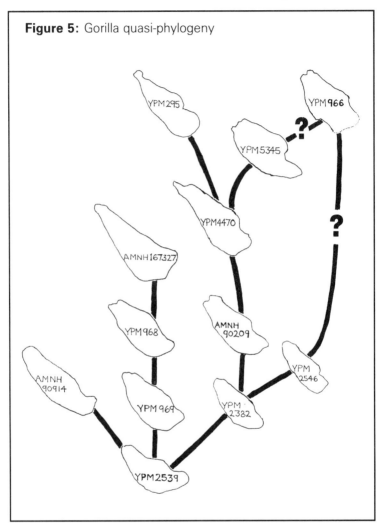

Figure 5: Gorilla quasi-phylogeny

ancestor? Elwyn Simons has pointed out that the cross-sectional shape of the ape lower jaw is 'notoriously variable' from individual to individual within the same species (Simons 1972, p.244). Figure 5 is based on outlines drawn by M. Goodman of Yale University, U.S.A. Those actual outlines show how highly variable the symphyseal region is in gorillas and strongly suggest that it is 'unreliable as a taxonomic indicator'. Simons further stated: 'Now that it is well established that the size of the simian shelf, its thickness at the superior transverse torus, and even its presence or absence vary widely within a given species of modern great apes, it seems inadvisable to give differences in such structures among fossils much taxonomic weight' (Simon 1972, p.245).

It should now be obvious why Leakey made a firm stand over refusing to allow 'Proconsul' to become merged with other species and become *Dryopithecus*. Those other species, unlike 'Proconsul', have simian shelves. By holding out against the opinions of equally worthy palaeoanthropologists Leakey tried to keep the door of evolutionary significance jammed open — at least in his own mind. Needless to say, other workers regard 'Proconsul' as being simply *Dryopithecus africanus* (Fig. 4).

Similar to the treatment given to 'Proconsul' is that afforded *Kenyapithecus wickeri*. It, too, has now been merged with other species of *Ramapithecus*. Elwyn Simons referred to it as *Ramapithecus wickeri*. Yet again, more recently, he has renamed it *Ramapithecus punjabicus* (Simons 1972, p.269). That last species includes *R. brevirostris*, which in turn was a synonym for an earlier species named *Dryopithecus punjabicus*.

In 1968 Leakey reasserted the validity of 'Proconsul' and transferred *Sivapithecus africanus* to the genus *Kenyapithecus* (Simons 1972, p.245). The upper jaw fragment representing this taxon had a large anteriorly curved and anterolaterally expanded front premolar. Le Gros Clark and Leakey described these features in 1951 and proposed that the creature possessed a large upper canine never found as part of the specimen. Then in 1965 Simons and Pilbeam drew attention to part of the cavity for a very large upper canine root. Their calculations showed that in life such a tooth would have had a cross-section of about 2 cm. With such large canines *Kenyapithecus africanus* can hardly have been a hominid (Simons 1972, p.246), yet Leakey had tried to make out that it was the oldest known hominid. Therefore this supposed twenty-million-year-old hominid widely touted by Leakey (Simons 1972, p.214) is an unlikely candidate for ancestry to Adam. These creatures, rather, are apes whose remains have come from Miocene deposits and which are devoid of hominid features.

Table 1: Olduvai hominid remains

Year Found	Cat. No.	Skeletal Parts	Species	Sex/Age	Site	Stratum
1913	OH-1	INTACT			RK	Naisiusiu
1935	2	Two parietale (f)			MNK	IV
1955	3	Teeth dc, dm2			BK	II
1959	4	L corpus mandibulae (f), M3 (or M2), isolated P & M (f)	H. habilis		MK	I
1959	5	Skull (calvaria & face)	Z. boisei	♂	FLK	—
1960	6	Parietale, teeth	H. habilis		FLK	—
1960	7	Parietalia (ff), mandibula, LI1-M2 RI1-M1	H. habilis	juv.	FLK	—
1960	8	Fingers, wrist and palm	H. habilis	juv.	FLK	—
1960	9	L. foot	H. erectus (leakeyi)	♂	LLK	II
		Calvaria (f)				
1961	10	Foot bone			FLK	—
1972	11	L. Palate, roots C-M2			DK	L.Ndutu
1963	12	Calotte (f), L. palate P3-M2 (all f)	H. erectus/ habilis		VEK	IV
1963	13	Calotte (ff), palate, teeth, mandibula	H. habilis	juv.	MNK	II
1963	14	R. parietale (ff), frontale (ff)		juv.♂	MNK	II
1963	15	Upper teeth RC, M3, LM3			MNK	II
1963	16	Calotte (ff), teeth	?H. habilis		FLK	II
1963	17	dm			FLK	
1963	19	M (f)	A. boisei	♂	FC (Stream bed)?	II
1955	20	Proximal diaphysis & neck of L. femur			HWK	II
1968	21	Upper LM1			FLK	?
1970?	22	Mandibula, teeth	of. H. erectus		?	IV

Year	No.	Description	Taxon	Sex	FLK	MASEK
1968	23	L. corpus mandibulae (ff) / Teeth P4-M2 (all abraded), roots P3				I
1968	24	Dished face, cranium, teeth	*H. habilis*	♀	DK	?
1968	25	L. parietale (f)			'54'	II
1966	26	Lower RM3			FLK	I
1969	27	Lower RM3			HWK	I
1970	28	L. femur diaphysis (f), L.os coxae (f)	*H. erectus/ habilis*		WK	IV
1969	29	Molar			JK	III
1969	30	Cranial fragments, teeth			FLK	II
1969	31	Lower RM1 or M2 (f)			HWK	I
1969	32	Upper dm 1(?)			MNK	II
1960?	33	Five fragments of parietale & occipitale			FLK	I
1962	34	Femur diaphysis (f), tibia diaphysis (f)			JK	III
1960	35	Tibia, fibula			FLK	I
1970	36	R. ulna			SC	II
1971	37	L. corpus mandibulae, teeth	*?Homo habilis*		FLK	II
1971	38	Lower RM2, L & R upper I1			SC	II
1969	39	Upper L dc-dm2 (all ff), I1-M2			HWK	I
1972	40	Upper R? M1(f)			FLK	II
1972	41	Upper LM1 or M2			HWK	II
1972	42	Upper RP3 or P4(f)			HWK	I
1960?	43	L. metalarsalia III and V			FLK	I
1970	44	Molar			FLK	I
1960?	45	Upper LM1			FLK	I
1960?	46	Probably distal part of crown of upper RP4			FLK	I
1960?	48	L. clavicula			FLK	I
1960?	49	Radius diaphysis (f)			FLK	I
1960?	50	Costa (f)			FLK	I
1960?	51	R. scaphoideum			FLK	I
1960?	52	L. capitatum			FLK	I

4. Catalogued specimens

It is sometimes refreshingly simple to refer to a particular fossil specimen by its catalogue number. Otherwise the name changes and taxonomic turmoil that surround species may blind or distract our attention from the often fragmentary nature of the material over which all the fuss is made. Also, having catalogue numbers based upon geographical locations does not prevent specimens from unrecorded stratigraphy being included for morphological comparison. Had all hominid bones been catalogued at the start of the twentieth century, it is doubtful whether the bones that made up the human portions of both Piltdown specimens would have deceived experts for so long. Dr Halstead has alleged that Dr Hinton of the Anthropology Department of the British Museum (Natural History) actually supplied some of the bones to the perpetrator of the Piltdown fraud.

A study of Table 1, which gives details of fifty Olduvai hominid specimens will reveal straight away that two originally listed are missing. They are OH 18 and OH 47, which are no longer regarded as being hominid.

Another aspect of the catalogued specimens is that only those included in the 1977 edition of *Catalogue of Fossil Hominids* (Part I) have been included. Doubtless more recent ones exist, but they are better left alone until detailed descriptions have been issued and carefully assessed. It seems prudent to hold back from reacting to every newly discovered specimen that the press sensationalizes as yet another nail in Adam's coffin. Many are so fragmentary that their most accurate epitaph is *'Hominidae indet'*. Alternatively, that could read *'incertae sedis'*, which is merely Latin for a fossil 'rag-bag'.

Where possible I have indicated the sex and species identification for the Olduvai specimens shown in Table 1. Also the stratigraphical position ascribed to each specimen, where known, is recorded along with the year in which it was found.

Naturally, particular specimens may be referred to by various names. For example, specimen OH 9 has been called 'Chellean Man', as well as *Homo leakeyi* (British Museum 1980, p.105). That is easier to appreciate than the fact that OH 7 is sometimes shown as having been found in Bed I and elsewhere depicted as coming from Upper Bed II (Wood 1978, p.42 (Fig. 4.1)). No doubt the further up the stratigraphic record the first found specimen of *Homo habilis* can be placed, the better some evolutionists would like it.

Table 2 is an attempt to compare specific skeletal remains from some African sites in order to see how those from Olduvai Gorge rate. In each case the 'Edenic total' includes bones from all parts of the skeleton excepting the teeth. The number of fossils consisting only of teeth is listed separately. It is of interest to note that the famous Olduvai Gorge had only thirty-eight non-tooth bones, which is the lowest score in Table 2. Even adding the twenty-five teeth specimens brings the combined total to only sixty-three. Other sites have considerably higher scores, except Ileret, where only eleven teeth specimens were found.

The total number of tooth specimens in Table 2 is 260. When the data for each site are turned into percentages based

FOSSIL REMAINS	Ileret			Koobi Fora			Olduvai Gge.			Sterkfontein			Swartkrans			TOTALS		
	No.	%	%	No.	%	%	No.	%	%	No.	%	%	No.	%	%	No.	%	%
skeleton				1	1	1	1	2	3							2	0.3	0.6
cranium	2	3	4	7	7	9	2	3	5	7	4	8	14	7	17	32	5.4	9.7
calvaria	1	2	2				1	2	3	5	3	6				7	1.2	2.1
calotte							3	5	8				1	1	1	4	0.7	1.2
mandibula	18	31	38	26	28	34	6	10	16	14	8	17	32	16	38	96	16.3	29.2
skull bones	9	15	19	14	15	18	10	16	26	32	19	39	24	12	29	89	15.1	27.1
vertebrae	1	2	2	1	1	.1				5	3	6	3	1	4	10	1.7	3.0
clavicula/costae							2	3	5							2	0.3	0.6
scapulae/coxae				1	1	1	1	2	3	4	2	5	3	1	4	9	1.5	2.7
long bones	14	24	30	23	24	30	7	11	18	10	6	12	5	2	6	59	10.0	17.9
manus/pedis	2	3	4	4	4	5	5	8	13	6	4	7	2	1	2	19	3.2	5.8
EDENIC TOTAL	47		99	77		99	38		100	83		100	84		101	329		99.9
teeth	11	19		17	18		25	40		87	51		120	59		260	44.1	
COMBINED TOT.	58	100		94	99		63	102		170	100		204	100		589	99.8	

Table 2: Specific skeletal remains incidence from some African sites

upon 260=100%, then from north to south, down the east side
of the continent of Africa, the percentages of tooth specimens
show an increase. Ileret starts with a low 4.2% and
Swartkrans finishes with a high 46.15%.

A speculative explanation of this trend is proposed as a
basis for further study. If the species involved lived mainly in
the vicinity of the Garden of Eden when the flood of Noah
occurred, and if Eden is, somewhat arbitrarily, located at a
particular point between the present Tigris and Euphrates
rivers, then the fossil remains may be related to the distance
they were carried by the Flood. Remains carried further
would be more fragmented and a higher proportion of such
remains would be found as durable dental material. Figure 6
displays this idea graphically. It shows the proportion of
dental remains plotted against the distance from 'Eden' and is
certainly consistent with this 'taphonomic' theory. (Tapho-
nomy refers to the history of animal remains from the time of
death to their reappearance as fossils.)

Figure 7 provides negative evidence bearing upon the real
age of hominid remains. This diagram shows chemical
analyses carried out upon bones included in the *Catalogue of
Fossil Hominids* (Parts I, II and III). The amounts of certain
chemicals found in these specimens are plotted against the
alleged ages of the specimens. There is no consistent change or
trend in the chemical parameters with supposed age, a
surprising result if the ages are indeed so different.

5. Correlated stratigraphy

Any discussion about alleged human evolution is bound to be
more dependent upon dating than upon the study of
comparative morphology of the actual fossil specimens (Wolpoff 1980, p.182). That is because it is generally accepted that
contemporaneous species are very unlikely to have an
ancestor-descendant relationship, whatever their similarities
or differences. What is just as important is that the supposed
ancestral form must be separated from the supposed descendant form by a time span long enough to have permitted the
hypothesized transformation.

One reason why evolution requires a lot of time is that the

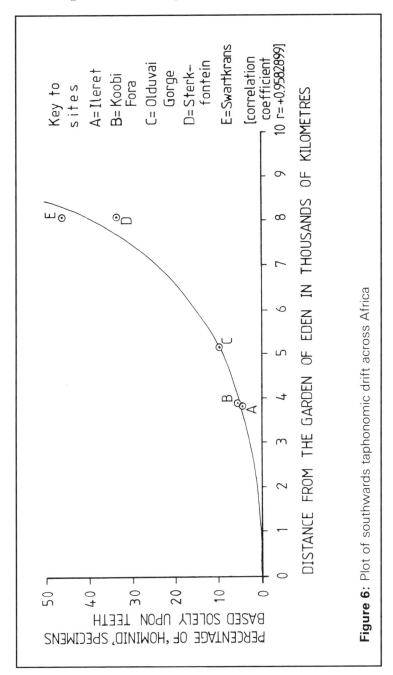

Figure 6: Plot of southwards taphonomic drift across Africa

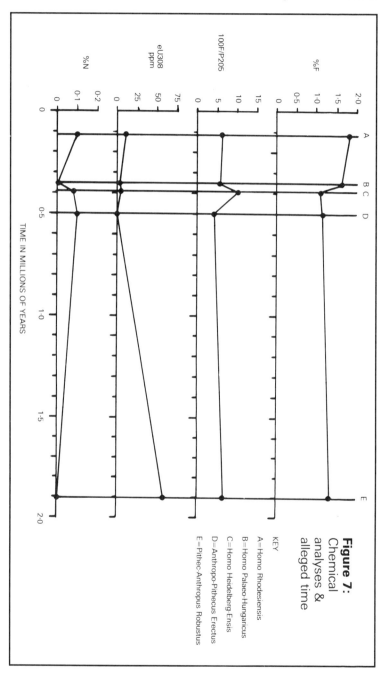

Figure 7:
Chemical
analyses &
alleged time

KEY

A=Homo Rhodesiensis

B=Homo Palaeo-Hungaricus

C=Homo Heidelberg Ensis

D=Anthropo-Pithecus Erectus

E=Pithec-Anthropus Robustus

TIME IN MILLIONS OF YEARS

process works very slowly and the requisite number of mutations must be enormous because the majority of them are deleterious. Another reason is that, given unlimited amounts of time, even the 'impossible' could just conceivably happen (or so it is claimed).

J. Haigh and J. Maynard Smith, both of Sussex University, tried to calculate the date of human origin. They reasoned that the first pair probably had identical haemoglobin in their red blood cells. After many generations and genetic mutations, today's human population should show much variation in the amino-acid sequence of this important respiratory pigment. Accepting that the mutation rate is about 10^{-9} per site per year (Haigh & Smith 1972, pp.73-89), variation by mutation should have occurred in about 15% of the possible sites if, as evolutionists suppose, man has been on this planet for a million years. Entirely unexpectedly, the two researchers found only 0.15% of people had a haemoglobin chain which differed from the normal. All the recorded variations in the haemoglobin of *Homo sapiens sapiens* could have occurred within a span of 10,000 years (Haigh & Smith 1972, pp.73-89).

It is admitted, then, that the assumed evolutionary past is not the key to the observable molecular present! At least, not if human haemoglobin is anything to go by. But how many evolutionist scientists admit that it has proved difficult to tie radiometric dates to sedimentary rocks whose exact position in the geological time scale is known? (Eicher 1976, pp.133-4.)

The core of the problem is that most of the 'accurate' radiometric dates are from igneous rocks that are difficult to define stratigraphically. Furthermore, the so-called geological systems involve sedimentary rocks that have been correlated, intercontinentally, by means of fossils (Eicher 1976, pp.133-4).

Figure 2 is an attempt to illustrate the stratigraphy of Olduvai Gorge and the vertical range of species and cultures with reference to the alleged time scale. Even more tentative and dubious is the attempt to correlate Olduvai Gorge with other sites in Africa as shown in Table 3 (based on Wolpoff 1980, p.160, Table 8.1). Although their relative stratigraphy appears to be accurate, no absolute dates are known for these important specimens and strata. Therefore the time scale should be treated with more than the proverbial pinch of salt.

The cause of the disarray over the time scale is a volcanic ash called 'tuff'. One specific tuff termed KBS (named after Kay Behren Smeyer) seems to have been the cause of much confusion (Wolpoff 1980, p.14). When it was tested by radiometric dating laboratories, different laboratories gave different dates for the KBS tuff samples from various parts of East Africa. That sampled from Turkana was dated at 2.6 million years, whereas that from Omo gave a date of 1.8 million years. What also disturbed palaeoanthropologists was the fact that corresponding fossils were similar in their alleged stage of evolutionary development. As Wolpoff pointed out, 'If the fauna evidence was correct, one of the dates was wrong. If the dates were correct, it took the faunal species three-quarters of a million years to spread fifty miles' (Wolpoff 1980, p.15).

Because the date of tuff found in Olduvai Gorge is similar to that from Omo, it is now believed that not all KBS tuff is the same. Therefore a compromise has been reached among evolutionists. It is to accept that some KBS is probably no older than 2.6 million years, and that some of what has been regarded as KBS is no younger than 1.6 million years (Wolpoff 1980, p.15).

The thought of rocks just over two and a half million years old having a proven inaccuracy of 1.0 million years must surely call in question the dating of allegedly older rock. At present it is hard on anyone who wants his fossil to be ranked as an ancestor of mankind if it was found associated with a younger tuff than someone else's find! This dating wrangle and the fragmentary nature of many hominid specimens fuel claim and counterclaim about human origins in Africa.

Whether any of the claimed dates are meaningful is seriously questioned by the fact that the Pliocene deposits in East Africa have produced hominid fossil specimens similar to the Pleistocene remains in terms of sample mean, size, range and morphology (Wolpoff 1980, p.154). Moreover, what can we really believe about the time represented by Beds I and II at Olduvai, when Wolpoff states that they represent 'a period of not more than 200,000 years' (Wolpoff 1980, p.167) and Koenigswald claims that a chronological gap of 'some 600,000 years' exists between them? (von Koenigswald 1976, p.76.)

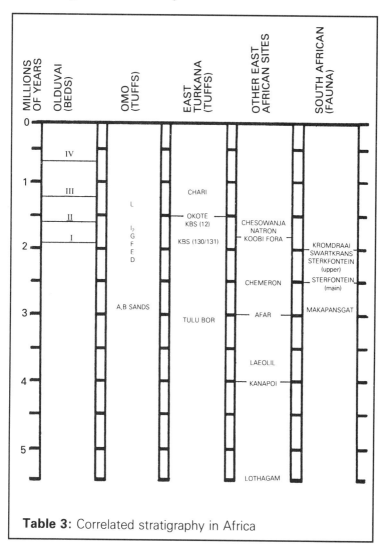

Table 3: Correlated stratigraphy in Africa

6. Confused speciation

Much confusion exists about the origin of species but in this section attention will be centred on the problem of hominid fossils in East and South Africa. There is more than one factor which compounds the problem of hominid speciation.

In the first place, doubts exist about the alleged course of speciation. Was it by one species diverging to become two separate species? Such a process is termed 'cladogenesis' and its proponents reckon that human evolution must have involved some branching of the hereditary family tree. Alternatively, others say speciation may have arisen when one species, instead of branching, gradually changed over a long period of time. This view is termed 'anagenesis'. I would like to call it 'phylometamorphosis', whereby successive generations are transformed as in the life history of a butterfly. Dr Leakey and like-minded workers pictured 'Proconsul' becoming *Kenyapithecus*, which led on to *Australopithecus*, from which the genus *Homo* is alleged to have arisen.

Whether an evolutionist expresses any commitment to the branching evolutionary model (cladogenesis) or the single-line evolutionary model (anagenesis), one species occupies a strategic position — it is *Homo habilis*. The most famous specimen is ER-1470, shown in Figure 4.

A whole series of fossils from Beds I and II of Olduvai have been combined into the single taxon *Homo habilis* by Leakey, Tobias and Napier (1964). Yet Wolpoff believes that the lower jaws should be treated as coming from two distinct forms (von Koenigswald, p.76). Certainly, questions about the validity of this taxon are probably more to do with the lack of really well-preserved remains and how best to interpret the specimens found.

One interpretation of *Homo habilis* fossils is that they represent a single lineage showing variation due to sexual dimorphism. In other words, some specimens are male and others are female. Another interpretation suggests that there are two types of jaws on account of adaptations to two different diets — some individuals being omnivores and others herbivores (Wolpoff 1980, p.181). A third interpretation is that three or more lineages are lumped together within the taxon (Wolpoff 1980, p.181). But those holding this third view are not agreed among themselves whether *Paranthropus* and *Zinjanthropus* should be combined to form the same branch or be kept apart to form separate branches.

Of course, anyone looking for evidence of hominid evolution can have a field day with fossil remains from Africa or, for that matter, Asia. As beauty is in the eye of the beholder, so too is evolution and especially incipient speciation. For instance, variations within present-day populations of apes could serve to concoct respectable-looking evolutionary schemes (an example is shown in Fig. 5).

Simons seems to be in agreement with the notion that variant contemporaries could substitute for apparent ancestors, but he added a cautionary note to round off his statement: 'It is a common and probably correct belief that anthropologists can find, without much searching, upper and lower molars in given modern ape skulls so similar to those of *Homo sapiens* that considered alone they probably could not be distinguished from molars of the latter species. This point is often presented as an example of the futility of trying to segregate known fossil hominoids into man-like and ape-like groups from teeth alone. What is missed by this reaction is that there are radically different proportionate relationships between the four different kinds of teeth in the two species *Homo sapiens* and *Pongo pygmaeus*' (Simons 1972, p.42).

Nevertheless von Koenigswald, who well knew the dangers of jumping to unwise conclusions on the basis of teeth alone, reckoned that even primate jaws do not on their own provide an adequate basis for firm conclusions (von Koenigswald 1976, p.55).

But the main complication, to my mind, does not centre around *Homo habilis* being a 'taxon whose time has come' (Wolpoff 1980, p.182), but rather has to do with the coexistence of specimens of the species *Homo erectus* within the same broad time span as *Homo habilis*. For instance, specimen 1813 is regarded as a female of *Homo habilis*. Another view is that it represents a gracile form of *Australopithecus africanus* (Wolpoff 1980, p.182). Dr R.E.F. Leakey (the son of Louis and Mary Leakey) holds to the second view, but by so doing implies that only the larger-brained (male?) specimens of australopithecines belong to the ancestral taxon, creating fresh problems (no females, no offspring!).

Then, of course, there is specimen ER 3733, which is undoubtedly *Homo erectus*. Wolpoff concedes that it may be the same age as ER 1813, or older, or younger! Apparently the problems of correlating dates over 700 square miles of the Lake Turkana site do not permit a more accurate view than that both existed within the same broad time span. That means that different views can be held by different experts. In addition to those already expressed, C.L. Brace and others believe that ER 1813 is a female *Homo erectus*. By implication they view ER 3733 as male (Wolpoff 1980, p.182). But what is particularly damaging to the idea that Africa is the cradle of human evolution is that the cranium of ER 3733 bears a striking resemblance to those found at Choukoutien in China (Wolpoff 1980, p.174).

Another problem has been identified by E. Mayr, C.L. Brace and later by M.H. Wolpoff. It is that the coexistence of different species of hominids cuts across the 'competitive exclusion' principle. At the very point of speciation competition exists between similar hominid forms. Yet neither extinction nor geographic separation occurred in South Africa in the Late Pliocene. So they argue that the similarities and degree of overlap between the South African samples were so great, when the total samples were considered, that no character divergence could be demonstrated (Wolpoff 1980, p.155). Therefore, because cladogenesis cannot be demonstrated, they believe that anagenesis must have happened. To my mind this is evolution having its cake in its hand after it has been eaten!

Probably in the popular presentation of evolution, people imagine that a species changes and this leads to the old and new forms not interbreeding. But the experts know that reproductive isolation must exist before any great morphological differences can arise. Also speciation is not deemed to have occurred until reproductive isolation is complete (Wolpoff 1980, p.27). Therefore because humans are a wide-ranging species, many authors feel that cladogenesis has rarely characterized human evolution (Wolpoff 1980, p.26). Also when descendant forms coexist with ancestral forms, it is equally difficult to believe in anagenesis.

There are many ingenious hypotheses about how mankind might have arisen. One is that early hominids took to eating seeds. Over many generations of using the tongue to lick seeds off their teeth and from between them, they gained the ability to move their tongues for speech. Of course, tongue mobility is used by man to produce many of the speech sounds, but the 'seed-eating' hypothesis (Wolpoff 1980, p.94) does not by itself account for tool use, bipedalism, canine reduction and intelligence (Wolpoff 1980, p.95). Another suggestion is the so-called 'killer-ape' hypothesis, where it is believed that broken bones were the first tools used by early hominids (Wolpoff 1980, p.91). But what tools did they use to kill, cut up and butcher the first animal?

As Wolpoff remarked, 'The problems surrounding the appearance of tool use and tool-making are equally cloudy; how long a period intervened between the earliest tools and earliest recognizable tools is unknown, and perhaps unknowable' (Wolpoff 1980, p.102). Elsewhere he wrote, 'No single hypothesis discussed above provides all of the answers to the problem of hominid origins. Indeed they do not always ask the same question' (Wolpoff 1980, p.95).

Therefore it would seem sensible to accept that the first man must have had everything that we reckon to be distinctively human. In the real world any half-measures would have produced a 'has been', not a human being.

7. Chipped stones

Not every chipped stone found in strata containing hominid fossils is necessarily an artefact. It could have been damaged by non-human intervention (a 'naturefact' rather than an 'artefact').

The so-called Kafuan culture was reckoned to have existed before the Oldowan culture in Africa. In fact, it was divided into four stages, which ranged from a split pebble 'tool' to one having a wavy cutting edge. Later it was realized that Kafuan tools could not be distinguished from naturally broken stones. Exit the Kafuan culture! (Wolpoff 1980, p.166.)

At present, the oldest stone-tool structures are ascribed to the Oldowan culture, named, of course, after the Olduvai area of East Africa. They can be distinguished from 'naturefacts' in two ways. One is that they have been flaked on both sides of any cutting edge. Another is that they usually consist of material not normally found at the site where they were discovered. In other words, the stones were shaped and used some distance from where they had first been collected (Wolpoff 1980, p.166). Incidentally, any item found away from its expected position could be a sign of human transportation. As such, the tool or other object is termed a 'manuport' (Wolpoff 1980, p.166).

The main feature of Oldowan tools is their rough and ready appearance. Wolpoff thinks that their classification into types of tools is a little spurious. He states: 'In addition, the so-called functional "types" may be more in the eyes of the beholders than in the intent of the australopithecines' (Wolpoff 1980, p.166).

What is a truly sobering fact is that present-day people have been observed making tools that are indistinguishable from those of the Oldowan culture (Wolpoff 1980, p.166). Therefore Oldowan tools cannot by themselves be used to give a relative date to any fossil find. What is also relevant here is that their presence should not lead anyone to conclude that a hominid specimen must have been the toolmaker. Remember this was the error made over the only complete human skeleton found in Olduvai Gorge, and again with Louis Leakey's original assessment of his wife's 1959 discovery of *Zinjanthropus* with artefacts (von Koenigswald 1976, p.74). That is why only the most advanced artefacts are used by excavators to date a particular site. Moreover, the quality of the end-product may be determined largely by the working quality of the original pebble or stone.

8. Covered sites

The reported discovery of so-called 'living floors' within the deposits of Olduvai seems as strange as it was unexpected. After all, who would wish to live or even stop for a few hours in a spot where sedimentation was occurring? One can accept that in some parts of the world it is a normal practice to live in wooden houses perched on stilts over a lake of water. A present-day parallel is a community working and possibly living on a sea-side pier complex. In the absence of regular refuse collections debris containing butchered bones would most likely be tipped over the side into the water. Within a primitive community it would be conceivable that, from time to time, the occasional artefact would accidentally be tossed into the water and no attempt made to retrieve it.

Apparently, however, 'living floors' are excavated camp

sites and a number have been found in various localities in East Africa (Wolpoff 1980, p.245). Some of the Oldowan sites show a pattern in the distribution of animal bones. There is a central circle containing bones that have been smashed into very small pieces. Beyond that are whole bones of animals which when freshly killed would have contained little marrow or even none at all. Therefore it is argued that the inner circle contained bones smashed to remove their marrow (Wolpoff 1980, p.167).

In Bed I at Olduvai only portions of the skeletons of large animals have been found, whereas there are complete skeletons of small species or very young individuals. Certainly that would support the hypothesis that most meat had been obtained by scavenging. But in lower Bed II a wider variety of sites exists. Some were for killing. Others were for butchering. Yet others were for collecting. Their interpretation points to improved hunting and better use of meat and bone marrow. Somewhere between Bed I and lower Bed II it is reckoned that hunting replaced scavenging (Wolpoff 1980, p.167). At least that was said to be the case in a textbook published in 1980 (Wolpoff 1980, p.168). Then in a 1982 review of the book (*Ancient Men and Modern Myths* by Lewis R. Binford) C.K. Brain stated that there was 'no evidence that Olduvai hominids hunted, or that they made use of base camps to which food was carried to be shared. Instead. . . [they were]. . . scavengers at discarded carnivore kills where hammerstones were used to break open leg bones to extract marrow' (Brain 1982, p.82).

Certainly a study of the precise position of each alleged covered site, both in terms of its geographical and stratigraphical location, would be worthwhile from the viewpoint of the uniformitarian, to see if the facts fit the explanation without exception. But more pressing is the need to explain such sites within the context of a biblical deluge framework.

Unless it has been clearly shown that living floors exist in storeys, one over the site of another below, then one possible explanation is that the sites are showing the topography before deluge sedimentation occurred to mummify such butchery sites with mud. That is, a site on high ground would be buried later than one on low ground and thus be found in a more 'recent' stratum.

This does not exclude the idea of development in hunting techniques, etc., since different sites, still exposed before the Flood, could be of different ages. Thus today Roman remains and modern ruins are both visible above ground and display great differences in culture!

But is there any evidence to suggest that the remains at Olduvai could be the result of a single cycle of sedimentation, as would be expected from 'flood geology'? Let us consider this question.

A glance at Table 1 shows how fragmentary are the skeletal remains of the Olduvai Gorge hominids. Only specimen OH 1 was intact. It is under suspicion of being an intrusive burial, so in that sense it stands apart from the other remains. Nevertheless, it can act as a useful comparison for evaluating the other specimens.

Table 4 itemizes the individual types of bone that contribute to the skeletal remains at Olduvai. There are fifty-six types listed and these are divided into eight categories, each category relating to a given portion of the skeleton. Isolated teeth are given a category of their own because of their frequency and importance. Each type of bone found will be awarded a 'score' of unity. Since a complete skeleton will have every type of bone present (except isolated teeth) it would have a total score of 49 points, and a category score of 7. The way points scores are obtained for the Olduvai specimens is detailed in Table 5. These scores range from 49 for the complete skeleton OH 1, to 1 for the isolated cranium specimen OH 36 and other single-bone specimens.

Using these results we can now define a 'bed skeletal index' as follows. We take the total points score for all specimens in a given bed and divide this total by the maximum points score per fossil (namely 56, including a score of 7 for isolated teeth) and also by the number of fossils present. The result is a figure which gives the actual points per bed as a fraction of the maximum possible points per bed. Call this fraction F.

A second number is produced by calculating the average number of categories per fossil. Thus a bed containing one foot bone and nine teeth would have two categories out of eight and ten specimens, giving an average category count of 0.2 for the bed. Call this figure G.

The bed skeletal index (BSI) is then defined as FxG (F

Table 4: Skeletal divisions

Cranial remains

t = isolated tooth/teeth

a	root	1
b	crown	1
c	incisor	1
d	canine	1
e	premolar	1
f	molar	1
g	upper or lower?	1
	TOTAL	7

D = dentary (lower jaw)

a	hinge	1
b	corpus	1
c	symphysis	1
d	incisor	1
e	canine	1
f	premolar	1
g	molar	1
	TOTAL	7

M = maxilla (upper jaw)

a	maxilla/alveolus	1
b	incisor	1
c	canine	1
d	premolar	1
e	molar	1
f	face/orbit/palate	1
g	frontal	1
	TOTAL	7

S = skull

a	whole bone or less	1
b	endocranial cast	1
c	calotte (skullcap)	1
d	calvaria (cranium)	1
e	face/frontal	1
f	brow ridge	1
g	foramen magnum	1
	TOTAL	7

Postcranial remains

F = fore-limb

a	humerus	1
b	ulna	1
c	radius	1
d	carpal	1
e	metacarpal	1
f	phalange	1
g	pollex	1
	TOTAL	7

T = trunk region

a	scapula/ilium	1
b	vertebra/sacrum	1
c	coccyx/tail	1
d	clavicle/ischium	1
e	rib/pubis	1
f	acetabulum	1
g	left & right	1
	TOTAL	7

L = leg (excluding foot)

a	femur head	1
b	femur neck	1
c	femur trochanter	1
d	femur shaft	1
e	patella	1
f	tibia	1
g	fibula	1
	TOTAL	7

f = foot

a	talus (heel)	1
b	calcaneus	1
c	naviculare	1
d	internal cuneiform	1
e	metatarsal	1
f	phalange	1
g	hallux	1
	TOTAL	7

Notes - an intact skeleton could have an endocranial cast which consists of mineral matrix within the brain-case yet it need not have any detached/loose/isolated tooth or teeth.

Table 5:
How remains shown in table 1 were transposed to table 4 scores

SPEC. OH	t	D	M	S	F	T	L	f	TOTAL SCORE
	abcdefg	abcdefg	abcdefg	abcdefg	abcdefg	abcdefg	abcdefg	abcdefg	SCORE
1	*******	*******	*******	•*******	*******	*******	*******	*******	49
2				*					1
3	•• * **								5
4	•• * **	*							6
5				***					4
6	•• •	*		*					4
7		* ****		*	****				10
8								*******	7
9				*					2
10								•	1
11			****	*					4
12			***	*					5
13			•• *	*					5
14				*	* *				2
15	•• * **			*					5
16	•• • *								5
17	•• • *								3
19	••								3
20							*		1
21	•• **								4
22		* ****							5

3 9 1 4 4 2 3 4 4 4 2 2 2 1 5 4 7 4 4 4 2 3 4 3 1 1 1 2 1

23 24 25 26 27 28 29 30 31 32 33 34 35 36 37 38 39 40 41 42 43 44 45 46 48 49 50 51 52

multiplied by G) and is a measure of the completeness of the skeletal remains in a bed. Thus one or more complete skeletons in a bed would have a points score of 49/56 and a 'category count' of 7/8. The BSI would then be 0.77 (not 1.00 because of the inclusion of isolated teeth as a separate category). This would in practice be the highest value and lower values would be obtained as the remains became more fragmentary. The factor F is a measure of the presence or absence of different bone types, while the factor G favours those beds in which the different categories of bone are well represented. Thus the BSI is an index of skeletal fragmentation (see Table 6).

When the BSI is plotted as a function of depth below the surface, an interesting and significant relationship emerges (Fig. 8). Apart from the intrusive burial in the Naisiusiu bed, which is not sedimentary in origin, the BSI values increase steadily with depth (i.e. with apparent age). *The deeper the bed, the more complete or less fragmented are the remains.*

This finding is very difficult to explain on a normal, uniformitarian, sedimentation model. It is, however, consistent with a flood model or single-cycle deposition. According

Table 6: Bed skeletal index parameters

Bed	Score (A)	Number of categories represented (B)	Number of skeleton specimens (C)	BSI $= \dfrac{A \times B}{56 \times C \times 8}$
Naisiusiu	49	7	1	BSI $= 0.77$
Lower Ndutu	4	1	1	BSI $= 0.01$
Masek	3	1	1	BSI $= 0.01$
III/IV*	18	8	6	BSI $= 0.05$
II	59	19	16	BSI $= 0.16$
I	81	27	22	BSI $= 0.22$

*It is customary to combine fossils in Beds III and IV.

to this scenario, the remains buried first would have been subjected to less damage than those carried about by flood waters for a longer period (or from a greater distance) before deposition.

Concluding summary

1. 'Nutcraker Man' and 'Handy Man' are examples of 'discoverer's bias' from Olduvai Gorge.

2. Australopithecines including 'Nutcracker Man' are now regarded as extinct forms of Southern Ape.

3. Bones found with tools could belong to the victim rather than to the hunter/maker.

4. Most of the radioactive minerals used for specimen dating come from igneous rocks whereas the fossil specimens come from sedimentary beds.

5. Beds I and II at Olduvai Gorge are alleged to have greater time gaps in them than the time span they are reckoned to represent.

6. Sexual dimorphism within the species *Homo habilis* could be mistaken for evolutionary branching.

7. Elsewhere in East Africa, skull ER 3733 has striking resemblances to 'Peking Man' and so suggests that Africa may not contain the oldest remains of early man.

8. Cladogenesis is largely ruled out of alleged human evolution because mankind is a wide-ranging species.

9. Anagenesis is the only alternative evolutionary process and that is ruled out by the apparent coexistence of alleged ancestor and alleged descendant species in Africa.

10. Mystery continues to exist over which human feature could first have arisen by evolution if they were not all present by special creation.

11. Tools reckoned to represent four stages in Kafuan culture are now regarded as natural breakages — they are 'nature-facts' instead of artefacts.

12. Present-day people have made tools indistinguishable from those allegedly belonging to the oldest Stone Age (Oldowan culture). So they cannot be used to date fossils.

13. Other things being equal, drowned corpses that became buried in lower strata would be more complete that those in higher strata. This is borne out by the facts.

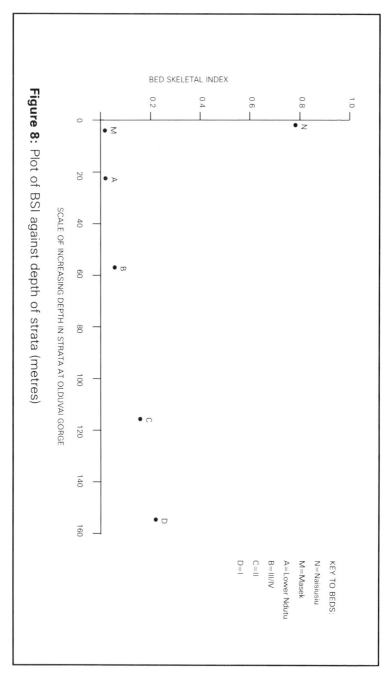

Figure 8: Plot of BSI against depth of strata (metres)

14. The most glaring presupposition in secular literature is summed up in the following statement by Eicher: 'In the geologic past there was no one around to observe the events and to write down what they saw' (Eicher 1976, p.20). Surely such a notion is true when applied to mankind. But it is inapplicable to the Originator of species, who challenged Job in a way that is relevant to geologists and philosophers. The Lord said, 'Where were you when I laid the earth's foundation?' (Job 38:4.)

Scientists who have come to an evolutionary impasse would do well to attend to what the God who *was* there when it all happened has recorded in Scripture.

'We accept the witness of man, but the witness of God is greater because it is the witness of God' (1 John 5:9).

Bibliography

The following sources were drawn upon to confirm certain points and comments in this present study. Most of them, in turn, have their own references to assist follow up. In no sense is this list meant to be a recommended reader's guide.

British Museum (Natural History) (1980), *Man's place in Evolution*.

Brain, C.K., (1982), Book review of *Ancient Men and Modern Myths* by Binford, A.L. *Nature*, vol. 295:82.

Campbell, B.G., (1978), Reviser of Third Edition of *The Fossil Evidence for Human Evolution*, University of Chicago Press.

Eicher, Don. L., (1976), *Geologic Time*, Second Edition Prentice-Hall International, Inc.

Goodman, M., unpublished work.

Haigh, J. & Smith, J. Maynard, (1972), *Genetical Research*, vol. 19:73-89.

Von Koenigswald, G.H.R., (1976), *The Evolution of Man*, Revised Edition, Ann Arbor, University of Michigan.

Laporte, Leo, F., (1979), Ancient Environments, Prentice-Hall International, Inc.

Leakey, L.S.B., (1968), 'Upper Miocene Primates from Kenya', *Nature*, vol. 218:527-528.

Leakey, L.S.B., Tobias, P.V. & Napier, J.R., (1964), 'A new species of the genus *Homo* from Olduvai Gorge', *Nature*, vol. 202:7-9.

Oakley, K.P. & Campbell, B.G., (1977), *Catalogue of Fossil Hominids*, Part I: Africa. Revised Edition. British Museum (Natural History), London.

Oakley, K.P., Campbell, B.G. & Molleson, T.I., (1971), *Catalogue of Fossil Hominids*, Part II: Europe. British Museum (Natural History), London.

Oakley, K.P., Campbell, B.G. & Molleson, T.I., (1975), *Catalogue of Fossil Hominids*, Part III: Americas, Asia & Australia. British Museum (Natural History), London.

Romer, A.S., (1966), *Vertebrate Paleontology*, Third Edition. University of Chicago Press, Chicago.

Simons, Elwyn L., (1972), *Primate Evolution: an introduction to man's place in nature*, Macmillan Publishing Co., Inc.

Wolpoff, Milford H., (1980), *Paleo-anthropology*, Alfred A. Knopf, New York.

Wood, B.A., (1978), *Human Evolution*, Chapman & Hall, London.

Part III

Scientific Concepts

7.

The concept of the species and its formation

Hendrik R. Murris

The purpose of this paper is to put the concept of a species into context with the creation model and the evolution model of origins. All kinds of questions can be considered including the following: What is the exact nature of a species? How constant, stable or unstable are species with respect to time? What capacity has an organism or species to adapt to a changing environment, to colonize a new environment or even to leave an unattractive environment? In other words, what is the variability of a species in relation to the environment? Which (micro-) evolutionary aspects are important for the creation model?

There are further questions. What is fact and what is hypothesis in the evolution model, and indeed in the creation model? What can really be observed, in nature or in the laboratory, in the fields of physiology of propagation, genetics and especially population genetics? These are all questions that have to be considered in education when dealing with the subject of origins.

Finally, it is in relation to the species and its formation that Darwin proposed his evolutionary theory or the doctrine of 'transformism'. It is necessary therefore to test this doctrine. What is valuable, and in agreement with the facts, has to be preserved, but unfounded phantasy and speculation must be recognized and rejected.

Fixism

By 'fixism' we mean a belief in the fixity of species. Many textbooks used in secondary schools deal with creationism as if it were synonymous with fixism, which in turn is viewed as an obsolete principle from the pre-Darwinian period.

Fixism is often formulated in an extreme manner which actually contradicts the Bible. In this form, it claims that God created all animal and vegetable species and these are still found in the locations where they have propagated unchanged since creation. Such a formulation completely ignores the Flood catastrophe, after which a new migration period must have begun. Genesis 9 and 10 records this as far as man is concerned, but it must also be valid for the land animals and even for plants. The reasoning of the extreme fixists is therefore incorrect according to biblical testimony. Animals and plants now found in Hawaii or the Andes have not propagated unchanged in these regions since creation, but can only have arrived after the Flood. Indeed, if fixism is presented in this extreme form proposed by certain followers of Linnaeus, then evolution actually appears the more credible theory!

Linnaeus

Linnaeus is often regarded as the father of fixism, but was this really the case? His work of classification, *Systema Naturae* (1735), is the best-known work in that field of the eighteenth century, and his contribution to biology is still invaluable. He introduced the binary nomenclature that is still followed faithfully today. He was greatly admired until after the beginning of the nineteenth century, but in our century he is criticized because he advocated the constancy of species. 'There are as many species as the Creator did create in the beginning.'

We have to realize, however, that a fixed outline of species really was necessary to create order in the chaotic systematics of that time. Every systematist introduced his own system and sometimes every variation was considered to be a new species. Linnaeus (1707-1776) decided to exclude those variations that resulted from environmental influence. Hooykaas (1976, p.176) has pointed out that Linnaeus was not, however, a rigid follower of fixism: 'Otherwise, he was not really as devoted to the constant nature of species as is often thought. His theoretical ideas developed and finally he came to believe that the original created species were much smaller in number than at present. By cross-breeding they should have increased in number and are perhaps still increasing. . . After he had created order in a slightly dogmatic way, the reins were thus loosened.'

As an example, Linnaeus wrote in 1767, 'We have to accept that therefore from the first vegetable principle the Creator has created as many different plants as there are natural orders. After this He Himself has mixed these plants by mutual propagation in such a way that as many plants developed as there are Genera at present. After this, nature has mixed and multiplied these plant Genera among each other by reciprocal propagation (which does not change the structure of the flowers).' This does not look very much like the fixism described in the textbooks, where species remain unchanged since creation at the location where they are now found!

Darwin and Mendel

Darwin (1809-1882), of course, rejected the fixity of species and formulated the changeability of species in its place. Since Darwin's discoveries during his voyage on the *Beagle* have been described enthusiastically in the textbooks, I shall not expand upon them here.

Although various evolutionary theories had been developed prior to Darwin, his was the first that was really successful. This was partly because of the enormous amount of data he produced and the better arguments that he mustered, but also because it suited the changing spirit of the times. Darwin had been working on the problem of the origin of species since 1839. According to his theory, the mechanism of speciation was based on natural selection, an idea he derived from Malthus' book *Essay on the principle of population* (1798). According to Malthus, the population increases faster than the means to support life. There is therefore a struggle for existence in which the strongest individuals survive. Darwin applied this idea to nature and made the following propositions.

1. There is variability. All animals and plants exist in an infinite number of variations. Note that he left the origin of these variations an open question.

2. There is a struggle for life and the fittest survive. That is, only those variations survive which, as a result of natural selection, have adjusted best to the external conditions. As with artificial selection, natural selection must also result in more perfect species by the establishment of favourable variations in the population.

According to Darwin, a species is what an experienced systematist, with a healthy judgement and specialized in the group concerned, offers as a species. During the time when the evolutionary theory was growing rapidly in popularity through the work of Darwin, and also of A.R. Wallace (1823-1913), nothing was known about the hereditary process itself. Strange as it may seem, the work of Mendel (1822-1884) received no attention. It has been suggested that this was because Mendel published his work in a little-known periodical, but this is not the case since the journal in question was known to various European universities. The neglect of Mendel's work should rather be attributed to the appearance of Darwin's book which commanded all the attention during that period. In 1985, the year of Mendel's publication, the time for genetics had apparently not arrived and its fundamental significance sank into oblivion. However, in 1900 his hereditary laws were rediscovered by De Vries, Correns and Tsjermak and have since been known as Mendel's laws. Thus it could be argued that Darwin's work caused a delay of thirty-five years in the development of modern biology.

Neo-Darwinism and creationism

Today in modern evolutionary theory, the mutation and combination of genes are of central importance. The mutation of hereditary factors, together with Darwinian natural selection, constitute the driving forces of evolution. This suggests that the source of genetic variation has been proven (a point which Darwin left open) and that natural selection completes the remaining part. This is misleading, however, since the origin of the hereditary properties of an organism or species still remain obscure.

Let us now confront the creation model with the evolutionary model. Two criticisms of the creation model are commonly made by evolutionists.

1. Creationists are accused of being purely negative, criticizing evolutionary theory without themselves making a positive contribution to the science of origins.

2. When creationists use the data of modern science in their creation model, e.g. when they admit the reality of micro-evolution, they are thought to be moving towards an evolutionary position and thus being inconsistent.

These criticisms are unjust. Evolutionists always claim that the actual data of modern science are proof of their model. If creationists seek to clear up this misconception it does not necessarily imply a criticism of every aspect of evolutionary theory. To the evolutionist it may appear to be criticism without contribution but this is a result of his own dogmatic thinking. The teachings of evolution are not the 'sole truth' and criticism is an essential part of the scientific process.

Regarding the second point, actual data must and can be used in the creation model but this does not mean that the creationist moves towards evolutionary theory in an inconsistent compromise. This point can be illustrated, in the context of this essay, as follows. Darwin made excellent observations and drew valid conclusions with respect to the variability of species, the struggle for life and natural selection. These are simple scientific data that can very well be applied in the creation model, as we shall see. However, the theory then developed by Darwin to account for the origin of larger systematic groups than the 'species' (his real transformation theory) is rejected by creationists. Since this theory is an integral part of the evolution model, the latter is also rejected by the creationist, who therefore makes no compromises. The first stage of Darwin's work, indicated as neo-Darwinism, is often called micro-evolution. The second stage, the so-called phylogeny, is called macro-evolution. *Micro-evolution really describes only the variability of the 'species' under the influence of nature*. Most 'species' are sufficently variable, as a result of their hereditary properties, to maintain themselves. In addition, *natural selection forms an important mechanism to 'clean' the gene pool from genes damaged by mutation*. Considered in this way, micro-evolution fits the creation model very well. Creationists do not move in the direction of the evolution model because they accept micro-evolution. Rather, creationists accept these data knowing that they are not adequate building-blocks for the evolution model! Evolutionists are in error when they obscure or reject the distinction between micro- and macro-evolution.

The modern concept of species

The propagation of organisms is the central point in this concept of species. At an early stage, Linnaeus himself chose propagation (of plants) as the distinguishing principle.

A biospecies must fulfil two criteria:

1. When crossing individuals, the offspring must be fertile (free, according to Mayr).

2. Propagation must take place freely in nature.

Consider an example. When a horse is crossed with a donkey (*Equus caballus* × *Equus asinus*) a descendant results which is highly viable and strong but which is infertile (a mule). The relationship between the parents is well represented by their common genus name, *Equus*, using the binary nomenclature of Linnaeus. In accordance with criterion 1, the horse and the donkey are different species. According to the same principle, on the other hand, all breeds of dog belong to the same species (*Canis familiaris*) in spite of the great external differences among them. Wolves (*C. lupus*) and dogs are different species according to criterion 2, in spite of the fact that fertile descendants have been obtained by crossing them. The same is true of song birds (for example, finch × canary). This is the reason why criterion 2 has to be included in the definition of a species.

The dual definition, however, still presents some problems and the naming of species remains somewhat artificial. It is possible to find species that exist as different populations in different areas and therefore cannot interbreed in nature.

According to the second criterion, they should receive different species names. Yet in a zoo, species A from Africa could be crossed with species B from Europe and give fertile offspring. Furthermore, A and B may differ greatly in appearance and still produce fertile offspring. Yet some species are named differently from others on the grounds of appearance only! The opposite may also occur. A and B live in the same area and look very much alike, but cannot actually cross-breed. Simpson calls these 'sibling species'.

Naming species, therefore, is far from simple. Every group of animals has its own differences in external characteristics and fertility. Furthermore, the crossing of animals with exoskeletons, such as insects, is much more difficult than with mammals and the criteria are correspondingly less easily tested and applied in such cases. However, although the taxonomists have not yet arrived at a final classification, satisfactory names have been given to the great majority of organisms. This is because the organisms show enough external differences to be distinguished from one another.

Some of the problems can be solved by calling the variations formed by the environment 'subspecies', 'eco-species', 'ecotypes' or 'races'. The choice of name depends somewhat on the individual scientist. If someone is inclined to distinguish as many species as possible, he is called a 'splitter'. On the other hand, a 'lumper' combines as many subspecies as possible. A real evolutionist, who hopes to observe a continuous gradual transition between species, will probably discover a 'new species' more readily than a creationist. The latter believes more in the constancy of species and will therefore explain all kinds of subdivisions as variations of the originally created species. The creationist is thus more of a 'lumper', and the evolutionist more of a 'splitter', though this does not always follow since the application of the criteria varies from person to person.

Fossil species

The criteria of fertile descendants and free propagation cannot, of course, be applied to fossils. The palaeontologist can only use the external shape of the fossil as a distinguishing criterion. This has resulted in a rather different, more morphological, concept of species (morphospecies) in palaeontology as compared with neontology. There are, of course, parallels in the two concepts, but in general the palaeontologist tends to be more of a 'splitter' than a biologist. This is certainly true for the period of time during which most of the arguments have been collected for the 'fossil leg' of the evolutionary theory. The resulting wealth of fossil species is presented in most textbooks for secondary schools and universities, as is illustrated in Figure 1.

The width of the 'drop-shaped' figures indicates the wealth of species and thus the 'success' of the animal group in relation to the column of geological periods. The extinction and revival of whole groups of organisms in such figures are presented as proof of evolution. But since the width of the figures reflects the number of species, or rather the number of species *names*, it is most important to know how much splitting has occurred per group of organisms. At one time, splitting was so exaggerated that new names were invented for fossils found in every minor stratum, and this excessive splitting unfortunately underlies most of the published 'drop-figures'. This may be helpful in correlating strata over a large area, but cannot fairly be used as a proof of evolution.

Fortunately, under the influence of modern statistical population research, a change of heart can be observed, and a considerable amount of 'lumping' has taken place. A lot of interesting information concerning the palaeontological concept of species can be found in the 1956 symposium *The species concept in palaeontology*. In one article (Ager, p.106) the author presents the example given in Figure 2 of a hypothetical 'evolutionary' process and states, 'One can never be sure that the apparent changes in characters with time, observed in one small area, are in fact evolution and not merely migration.' This idea of migration-with-change might be of value for the catastrophic sub-model within the creation model. Flood geology could equally well attribute this 'migration' to a sedimentation process.

There has been an improvement in recent years in the 'jungle of names' that previously characterized palaeontology. No longer does every organism obtain a separate name depending on (for example) the number of spots, as in Figure

Figure 1
Diagram of the 'evolution' of vertebrates. Figures in millions of years.

2, or on the strata in which it is found, or even on the desire of the discoverer for glory! There is now a genuine attempt to find the common characteristics of a species within the limits of its variability. 'Primitive men', 'ape-men', 'man apes' and similar fossil individuals with names like *Paranthropus, Zinjanthropus, Australopithecus* etc., were once all presented as possible

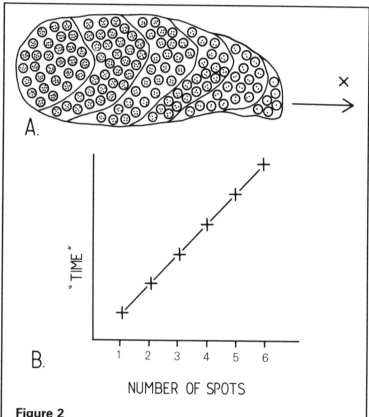

Figure 2
A. Chart of the distribution of the variations of a hypothetical species with 1, 2, 3, 4, 5 or 6 spots. The arrow shows the direction of the migration of the species along a location 'X'.
B. Graphic depiction of the gathered individuals from consecutive strata of location 'X'. In this way the graph shows an apparent evolutionary trend of forms with one spot to forms (morphs) with six spots.
(Ager, 1956)

ancestors of man, but have now been lumped as varieties of *Australopithecus*. Similarly, *Pithecanthropus, Sinanthropus* etc. are now considered as *Homo erectus*.

Thus recent palaeontology has curbed the inclination to split and it only remains for the 'drop-like' figures in the textbooks to be corrected so that they do more justice to the fossil discoveries themselves. I doubt, however, whether supporters of evolution will be eager to make this correction. Time alone will tell. The argument that many more species existed in the past than do at present, and therefore evolution must be true, has been weakened considerably by these developments.

Finally, it should be noted that because of the nature of its material, palaeontology cannot progress further than the distinction of a morphospecies and sometimes a chronospecies (a morphospecies that is found as variations in consecutive strata).

Formation of species

If the criterion for the distinction of two species is whether the descendants are fertile or not when crossed, it is necessary to investigate how *reproductive isolation* might arise. It is also necessary to investigate whether hereditary material can be transferred from one population to another. In this connection, population genetics are concerned with gene exchange between the various populations. This is illustrated in Figure 3.

Population genetics takes a rather different approach from classical ('textbook') genetics. According to Mendel, genetics are concerned with the *number of individuals* of a distinct genotype and phenotype in the various generations of descendants. Population genetics, on the other hand, are concerned with the *number of genes* in a certain population. Any gene exists in a number of alleles and the frequency of alleles is the point of interest and investigation. To a population geneticist, the population consists of a 'gene pool', in which every gene can be changed by mutation. Then one can try to measure the success of a gene, or a mutated gene, through successive generations under the influence of natural or artificial selection.

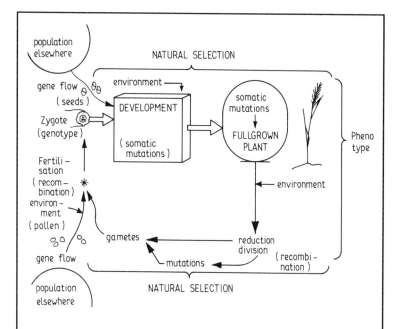

Figure 3

Schematic representation of the interaction of various processes, which can introduce variations in a population (seedplants). The first cell of an organism (zygote) is the result of the fusion of two germcells (gametes). The zygote could develop to a mature full-grown plant through the complex and little known process of the development (presented in the figure as a 'black box'). The various environmental factors will determine which one of the genetic possibilities of the genotype will ultimately be manifest in the phenotype, the external appearance of the full-grown, mature plant. The natural selection then has such an influence that, for instance, some of the genotypes do not develop into mature plants. These plants do not pass on their genes to the next generation, while other plants do pass on their genes. During the reduction division at the formation of the gametes and the fertilization new combinations of genes can result. The genes can mutate during every stage of the cycle; however, only those mutations that can be passed on through the gametes can have some effect on the change of the species (micro-evolution).

The mutations in the tissues (somatic mutations) have practically only an influence on (a part of) the individual itself. (Only if that particular mutated part were released at non-sexual propagation can the mutant play a possible part in the population.)

Finally through the introduction of pollen and/or seed from other populations gene flow takes place.
(Based on O.T. Solbrig, 1970, modified).

It is important to distinguish which mode of selection affects such a population of alleles. Three different modes of selection are recognized and these will be discussed with the help of Figure 4. We shall also discuss critically some practical examples which are used as 'proofs' of evolution. In the course of this discussion we shall see the 'dynamic' character of a species with respect to its environment, as well as its stability or constancy. The creationist concept of species will be shown to agree well with the reality observed in nature.

A closer look at natural selection

Many examples described as 'evolution in action' or 'evolution right before our eyes' (Julian Huxley) appear to be nothing more than natural selection in action. Natural selection itself, of course, is not evolution! The effects of natural selection on a population of organisms are observable, but the possible (micro-) evolution can only be deduced. How far can such environmentally induced changes in a population be explained by variation, in the sense of the creation model (1), and how far do they demonstrate micro-evolution in the sense of the evolutionary model? Put differently, we may ask two questions: how dynamic is the genotype and the phenotype of the created species in relation to its natural environment, and what are the limits of such variations? To what extent can, or should, a biospecies change under the influence of the environment in order to be called a new biospecies? Let us consider some practical examples with the help of Figure 4.

Stabilizing selection
This has been defined as discrimination against phenotypically peripheral individual members of a population by means of natural selection (Mayr 1963). This type of selection can also be called centripetal (Simpson 1953) or normalizing selection (Waddington 1957). In this situation the selection acts in such a way that a certain optimal phenotype endures (Fig. 4a I-II). Every deviation from the average has less chance to pass on its hereditary properties to the next generation.

This type of selection is generally found in nature and many examples can be cited. A classic example is from A.C. Bumpus (1896), who studied sparrows caught in a heavy blizzard. The surviving sparrows appeared to be those with characteristics closest to the average for this species. The same characteristics varied much more strongly in the sparrows that perished. Again, in hibernating populations of common wasps, the extreme variations were eliminated during the winter. As a result the variability of the spring population was

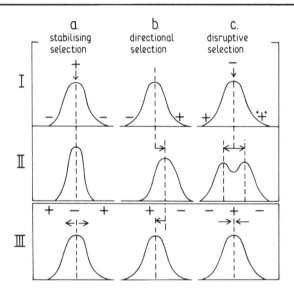

Figure 4

The three main types of selection and the change to be expected in genetic variation in consecutive generations.

I Start of the selection;
II after various generations;
III possible result of reversed selections (compared to I) after still more generations.

'−' is the disadvantageous and
'+' is the favouring selection pressure on the various parts of the population and thus also on the genes which survive with more or less success in the following generations.

The vertical axis represents the frequency of the individuals in every population; the horizontal axis represents the phenotypical variation of the population.

strongly reduced relative to that of the preceding autumn (Thompson *et. al.* 1911).

It appears that with stabilizing selection, a strong (abiotic) environmental factor acts as a 'bottleneck' for survival; exceptional phenotypes do not get through, and the species is thrown back upon its average properties. For example, deviations caused by mutations are eliminated effectively in this way. If the abiotic factor (e.g. climate) is more gentle during the following years, then the population may expand to a larger variability. Some extremes may even acquire a temporary advantage under the influence of different selective factors. This is illustrated in Figure 4a III. This kind of selection appears to be a common natural phenomenon, though this is not brought out in the evolutionary literature. The results of stabilizing selection are not attractive to the evolutionist because nothing changes and the species remains constant. For the same reason, this form of selection supports the arguments of the creationist.

Directional selection

By contrast, the second kind of selection, *directional selection* (Fig. 4b), is attractive for the evolution model and this is probably the reason that so many examples have been described in the literature. A wealth of literature on the subject, however, does not mean that this kind of selection occurs more commonly than others. If a researcher is trying to observe evolution in nature, then he looks for these kinds of examples and can easily overlook examples of less interest to him.

In directional selection, a shifting environmental factor causes a change in genotypical frequencies, till a new balance is reached (Fig. 4b I-II). As in stabilizing selection, a single optimum has been achieved, but the favoured phenotypes ('+') are different from those of the average class. One of the best-known and most dramatic cases of this form of selection is industrial melanism in moths (Fig. 5). This phenomenon has been observed in at least eighty British and forty North American species.

White-spotted moths are well camouflaged against predation by birds as long as they are resting on tree trunks covered by lichens whose colouration they mimic. With the advent of industrial pollution, the lichen cover disappeared and the tree trunks darkened. The white-spotted moths were no longer concealed and the species might have disappeared in the affected areas if a dark-coloured form had not taken its place. The dark 'carbonaria' moth was almost invisible to the predating birds. J. Huxley called it 'evolution before our eyes'.

However, as air pollution was reduced, the lichens re-

Figure 5
Spotted moths (*Bison betularia*) on dark bark (i and ii) and spotted bark (iii).

covered and the dark-coloured variety became the more disadvantaged. Consequently the white-spotted variety returned to the areas concerned (Refer, among others, Kettlewell 1953: Tinbergen 1978). Immigration of white-spotted moths from neighbouring areas was the main reason, but 'reversed mutation' should not be discarded. Could this be evolution in the reverse direction? (Fig. 4b I-II followed by II-III.)

It seems much more likely that the variously camouflaged phenotypes belong to the common variability of the species, a variability that can perhaps be widened (temporarily) by an easily mutating group of genes. The flexibility of the species co-operates extremely well with the changing environmental conditions. All kinds of camouflage in nature can be included within this selection mechanism. Is this 'evolution', or is it the natural behaviour of created species responding dynamically to a hostile and changing environment for the purpose of self-preservation?

Disruptive selection
According to this third selective mechanism (Fig. 4c), multiple selective forces favour two or more diverse phenotypes and discriminate against intermediate ones. This kind of selection leads to a discontinuous variation which ends up either in (1) polymorphism or (2) divergence through isolation or sympatric speciation (see later). In polymorphism, each selective optimum of a given population has a different appearance. The whole population, however, remains structurally intact. Consider some examples.

Certain insects mimic others which are inedible or deterrent in some other way. For example, tiger swallowtail butterflies (*Papilio glaucus*) are excellent food and are therefore preferred by birds (see Fig. 6). There are two types of female individuals. Some have brown stripes against the yellow background of the wings (Fig. 6b), similar to the males (Fig. 6e), but others are dark (Fig. 6c). The latter resemble (mimic) another butterfly, *Battus philenor* (pipe-vine swallowtail, Fig. 6a), which has an unpleasant taste. Birds learn to avoid *Battus* and therefore also avoid the edible dark variety of *Papilio*.

One would expect the imitative variety of female to prevail,

a Pipe-vine swallowtail
Battus philenor
female

d Pipe-vine swallowtail
male

b Tiger swallowtail
Papilio glaucus
female

e Tiger swallowtail
male

c Tiger swallowtail
mimic female

Figure 6
(Based on *'Origin of Species'*, 1981.)

but this appears not to be the case. If at a given moment there are many more dark *Papilio* than *Battus* the birds no longer learn to avoid them, since most of the dark-coloured moths they catch are edible! This kind of mimicry, therefore, is not under a constant selective pressure. It all depends on the relative numbers of *Papilio* and *Battus*. This form of polymorphism has been called 'balanced polymorphism' (Figure 4c I-II followed by II-III).

Another kind of *Papilio* shows this phenomenon even more strongly. It has been discovered that the females of *P. dardanus* (the mocker swallowtail) imitate three different inedible butterfly types! The reason that males do not exhibit the same kind of mimicry is probably that differently marked or coloured males would not be recognized by females as mating partners. Thus the common markings (yellow with brown spots) of the male *Papilio* always remain constant in the population.

Is this again 'evolution in action'? According to my view, this is really another example of the way a created species adjusts dynamically to its environment.

Certain snails (*Cepaea nemoralis*) can have extremely variable coloured and ringed shells. As a species, therefore, they possess camouflage for every type of background. This situation seems to be maintained by the third type of selection, each colour variation being favoured by a particular background. A complication arises in this case from the behaviour of the birds that prey upon them. It is well known that birds may develop a 'search image' of their favourite food (see e.g. Croze 1970), and this is likely to be the case for snail-eating birds. A foraging bird can cover a much larger area than a sub-population of snails because of the latter's slow rate of migration. Such a bird may develop a 'search image' consisting of a certain pattern of rings because there happens to be a large number of such individuals present. Discrimination against these individuals will result (Fig. 4c I'—'), while other snails go unrecognized and are therefore able to pass on their genes ('+'). Given time, the latter snails increase in numbers and situation 4c II results. If now the new 'frequent' varieties of snail give rise to new search patterns in the predators, they in turn will be at risk and the situation may return to that shown in Figure 4c III (a single optimum form). Thus the intrinsic variability of *Cepea* is preserved and is an important condition for survival of the species as a whole.

All three types of selection in the long run do not, therefore, cause a real change in the species. A kind of *status quo* is maintained as a result of the innate variability of the species. This is an important point for the creation model. Such 'co-operation' of varieties and even of mutations with natural selection is not capable of providing a driving force for macro-evolution. The phenomenon of micro-evolution in the evolutionary model, on the other hand, cannot be distinguished from the dynamic variability of created species in relation to their environments which is an intrinsic part of the creation model.

Natural preservation of variability

Sometimes a heterozygote has an advantage over both the homozygotes (Aa as opposed to aa and AA). The result is that both alleles (a and A) are maintained in the population. This effect is called 'heterosis'. An example is human sickle-cell anaemia. Genotype AA has normal blood cells but is vulnerable to malaria in tropical areas. Genotype aa has sickle-cells and dies early as a result of inadequate oxygen transport by the blood. Genotype Aa has only a few sickle-cells but is immune to malaria. So the deleterious allele 'a' is maintained in the population.

A second example is the so-called 'effect of rarity'. This was first described by Petit in 1958 for *Drosophila melanogoster,* and has been found subsequently for other types of fruit flies (see e.g. Ehrman, 1965). It appears that, in a population of fruit flies consisting of various genotypes, a mating preference sometimes exists for those genotypes which are present in small numbers. Obviously, this helps to preserve rare alleles and therefore to maintain variability in the species. Evolutionists have not yet been able to offer an explanation for this effect.

Speciation by the isolation of populations

In modern ecology, the migration of organisms takes on an

important role. Previously it was assumed that propagation factors (seed, spores, 'germs') 'were present everywhere and that the environment was selecting'. In micro-biology this assumption is still, to a large extent, accepted. As a result, the emphasis was placed on abiotic factors and the tolerance of the organism to them.

The pattern of dispersion of organisms on earth is, however, much more complicated than this concept allows. The 'germs' of an organism are not 'everywhere'. They have to arrive from 'somewhere'. That is, there must be migration and this means that one kind of organism can have a greater dispersal (active or passive migration) than another. Whether, after this migration, the organism makes a good start in the new location depends upon several factors, including habitat selection and the behaviour of other organisms already present. Only after this will abiotic factors become significant in their influence.

C.J. Krebs (1972, p.16) explains it in this way: 'Why are organisms of a particular species present in some places and absent from others? To answer this question we look for differences between areas occupied and areas not occupied. This can be done in several ways and one method of attack is to proceed sequentially through the following steps (Macan, 1963)'.

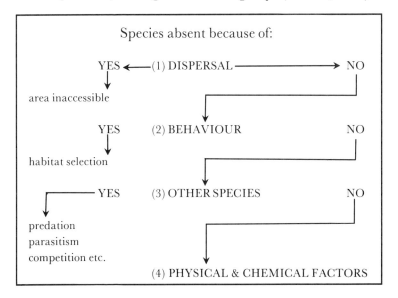

Very many organisms certainly have a large variability which enables them to adjust to a range of different environments. This was made clear in the previous discussion. This leads us to consider the fact that migration (or dispersal) and speciation are closely connected. This is particularly interesting for the creation model in which the world-wide catastrophe of the Flood plays an important role. Following this catastrophe, the world must have been repopulated starting from one, or a very few, locations and by very few individuals per species. It could thus easily happen that small populations became isolated from one another and rapid speciation was possible. What are the principles governing such a process?

Suppose for some reason a population with a particular gene pool becomes split into two or more parts. Each of the resulting sub-populations goes its own way (Figs. 7 and 8). During this period, when there is no gene exchange between them, the genetic composition of each sub-population can change by the types of natural selection discussed above. It is also possible that at the time of separation the gene composition of the sub-populations was already differently distributed. A third possibility is the loss of genes by chance in small isolated sub-populations ('genetic drift'). If after a certain time (a period no longer than 100 to 2000 years seems necessary) the sub-populations meet again but do not interbreed, then according to our definition of a biospecies, two new such species have been formed. The following divisions can be made according to the original cause of population splitting.

a) Geographical barriers (Fig. 7)
Examples are the formation of a mountain ridge, a strait between two continents, a land bridge between two continents or between lakes or seas due to a drop in water level (separating marine species).

b) Ecological barriers (Fig. 8)
Sub-populations propagate in different seasons or habitats.

c) Migration (dispersal) behaviour

A possible example of speciation casued by a geographical barrier (a) in combination with migatory behaviour (c) is afforded by great tits. This may be deduced from their current distribution pattern (Fig. 9) according to which two types of great tit in the Far East do not recognize each other as the same species. This is sometimes cited as evidence for evolution, but the following hypothesis provides an alternative explanation that is consistent with the creation model.

The original population, after the Flood, occupied a region south of the Caspian sea. Some birds migrated eastwards and some to the north and west. The two groups thus travelled by

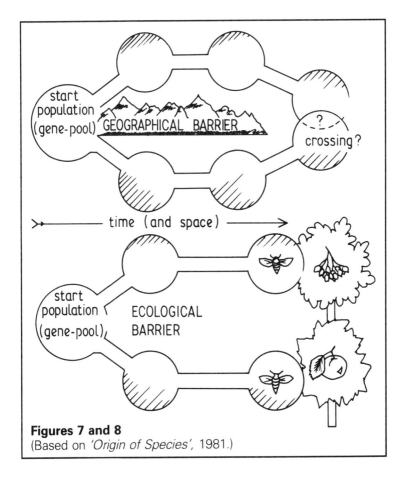

Figures 7 and 8
(Based on *'Origin of Species'*, 1981.)

different routes around mountain barriers such as the
Himalayas, colonizing areas as they went and increasing in
numbers with time. After many generations, this process of
dispersal brought them together again in the Far East. When
this occurred, they no longer recognized each other as mating
partners because of variations in colour, song, behaviour etc.
They had, indeed, become separate biospecies according to
our definition, but the process has no implications for macro-
evolution.

It also appears that an ecological barrier can split a
population. This has been described for various insect species.
The life-cycle of an insect is generally very short and several
generations can succeed one another within one year. A
change in the environment can thus produce rapid conse-

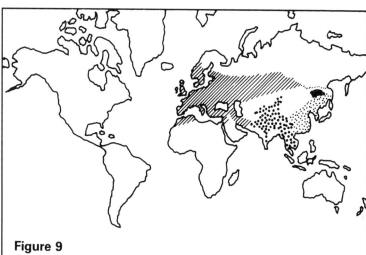

Figure 9
Dispersion pattern of great tits. In the striped and dotted areas
the tits mate, in the black area they do not.

  Parus maior maior

  P. maior bakharensis

  P. maior minor

  P. m. maior and P. m. minor live together like
different species.

quences. The North American fruit fly, *Rhagoletis pomonella*, has divided into two populations which depend on different trees in the same area. One lives on hawthorns and the other on apple trees, and they do not cross-breed. How could this situation arise? More than a century ago, there were only 'hawthorn flies'. The females laid their eggs in August on the hawthorns and at the end of September and into October, the larvae fed on the red fruits. Later, some apple trees were introduced in the area. A few flies reproduced in July and laid eggs on the apple trees. During September, the resulting larvae fed on apples, which ripen earlier than hawthorn fruit. A new population, dependent on the apple tree, thus became established and no longer crossed in the wild with the original population due to a one-month difference in mating period. The hawthorn and apple flies, however, are still capable of mating and still look exactly alike! Since gene exchange no longer occurs, the two populations may eventually develop into separate species according to our definition. (*Origin of Species*, (1981), British Museum of Natural History.)

Genetic drift

Up to now we have considered forces that can change the gene frequencies of a species in a particular direction, namely the (natural) selection of pheno- and geno-types arising from variation plus mutation and migration. There are also forces which can change gene frequencies in a totally undirected manner and the most important of these is 'random genetic drift'.

If a population is very large, the gene frequencies will not change significantly from generation to generation, being maintained according to the Hardy-Weinberg principle (1908). However, the smaller the population, the more readily may genes fail to be passed on to the next generation. A given gene may not be present in the germ cells fusing to form a zygote. In large populations sufficient zygotes are formed to guarantee preservation of all genes in the gene pool, but this is not necessarily so for small populations. Obviously, a small group of, say, fifty humans does not collectively possess all the genes present in the human race. Furthermore, one reproduc-

tive cell of a given individual does not possess every gene of
that person, because of the 'reduction division' of such cells.
The children actually produced within a small colony of individuals do not therefore possess all the genes of the original
group, even collectively.

This genetic drift (the chance loss of genes from generation
to generation in small populations) can be simulated using a
game computer and Figure 10 shows the result of one such
experiment. In this particular case, out of 400 hypothetical
populations of only eight (diploid) individuals each, four pairs
of two individuals per generation were chosen randomly. The
number of descendants per pair varied but was, on average,
two. Each population started with a 'gene pool' of two AA,
four Aa and two aa individuals, so that every population
started with each allele present as 50% of the total.

Evaluating the result after thirty-two generations, it
appeared that most of the populations were homozygote (AA
or aa). Of course, a population that is wholly AA has lost the
allele 'a' and vice versa (Mettler & Gregg 1969, p.53).
Suppose that (as an over-simplified example) the allele 'A'

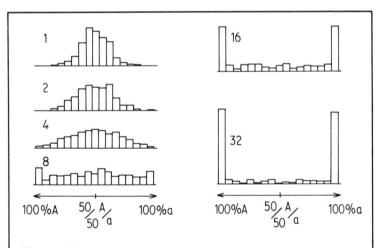

Figure 10
Result of a 'monte carlo' computer game of 400 hypothetical
populations of 8 individuals after many generations.
(Based on Mettler and Gregg, 1969).

imparts the ability to fly in a bird species, while 'a' signifies flightlessness. If birds with AA and Aa combinations arrive and breed on an island where they have no natural enemies, the flightless aa individuals which will inevitably be hatched will survive. Some generations later, according to our model experiment, the entire population could be flightless!

There is, in fact, a recorded example where this seems to have taken place. Ornithologist W. Oliver tells the story of the flightless wrens of Stephen Island near New Zealand (Fig. 11). 'In 1894 the lighthouse-keeper's cat brought in eleven specimens, which came into the hands of H.H. Travers. . . A few more captures made and duly reported by the cat and then no more birds were brought in. It is evident, therefore, that the cat which discovered the species also immediately exterminated it' (S. Carlquist, 1965).

This mechanism is not, of course, valid for all flightless birds. Some species, such as the ostriches and penguins, are so original that they can only have originated from created archetypes. Furthermore, it should be clear that this genetic drift results in nothing new. It is rather a form of degeneration and only mild environmental conditions would allow such impoverished variations to survive.

In large populations, the Hardy-Weinberg law applies and hardly any genetic drift occurs. This law states that gene frequencies remain constant in a population, providing the genes concerned have as much advantage as disadvantage for the carriers. This has been investigated for human blood groups. It has been shown that small human tribes, like Eskimos or Australian Aborigines, possess fewer different blood groups than larger populations. This can be attributed to genetic drift as a result of inbreeding. If such inbreeding occurred among the Darwin finches of the Galapagos Archipelago, it would have produced the various subspecies found there much more rapidly than would natural selection. (But note that G.H. Harper [1980] has proposed yet another mechanism for the differences between finch species in the Galapagos, based upon migration with the different islands viewed as 'targets'. We cannot review this mechanism here but those who teach biology will find Harper's article an excellent basis for critical discussion.)

It should now be clear that the traditional neo-Darwinian

'driving forces' for evolution are not the only possible causes of speciation. Races, subspecies and biospecies (by our definition) can be formed much more rapidly than in millions of years. The whole matter is very complex but, according to creationists, micro-evolution goes no further than the limits of variation of the dynamic created 'kinds' will allow. Micro-evolution cannot be extrapolated to macro-evolution or phylogenesis because it is an essentially limited process.

The creationist concept of species

It will have become clear that at present creationists and evolutionists have similar views regarding the 'biospecies' and its mode of formation. The creation model accepts the importance of propagation barriers, such as different habitats, reproduction in different seasons, differences in appearance or behaviour, physiological differences in the reproductive cells and sterile descendants. The creation and evolution models do, however, differ concerning the speed at which speciation can occur. In the evolution model millions of years are

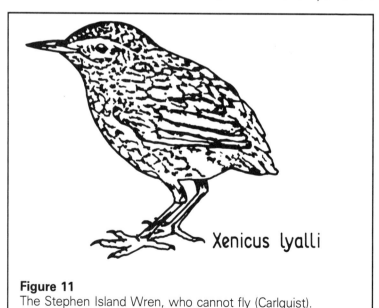

Xenicus lyalli

Figure 11
The Stephen Island Wren, who cannot fly (Carlquist).

typically 'required' for the creation of a geographical barrier and the resulting species formation; the creation model calls for only a few hundreds or thousands of years.

A second and fundamental difference between the two models is the origin of the archetypes of the present biospecies. The work of Professor F.L. Marsh in this field is very important for creationists. (Marsh is one of the few creationist biologists who is taken seriously; see, for example, Dobzhansky, 1951). According to Marsh, the archetype of the present biospecies is the 'baramin' (*bara*=to create; *min*= kind), and a given baramin has a large number of related species. Further, the biblical words 'after its kind' can also be understood to mean 'after its variety of species' (compare Ouweneel, 1976). Thus Marsh proposes that, apart from mankind, organisms were created polytypically, that is to say in two or more varieties (1947, p.178 *et seq.*). This is shown in Figure 12.

This diagram also shows the effect of the biblical Flood, in which many kinds perished. Those that survived 'microevolved' during the following millennia to the presently known species. It must be emphasized that discontinuity plays a major role in the creationist concept of kinds. Thus, for example, the cat family (cat-kind) can be understood as one polytypical baramin and the dogs (dog-kind) as another. Dog and cat are therefore not related even though, systematically, they both belong to the order *Carnivora,* or even more widely to the mammals. Their similarities are attributed to the basic plan of the Creator and not to phylogenetic relationships. Marsh proposed a fertilization test to reveal whether species are related to the same baramin. If a male sex cell from one species can fuse with a female ovum from another under simulated natural circumstances in the laboratory, and if chromosome pairing occurs followed by cell division, then the two species must be related to the same created kind. Such an experiment is not really necessary in practice since the discontinuity of the different baramins is normally self-evident from the external appearance of the organisms (for example, the cat- and dog-kinds referred to above). S. Scherer has coined the term 'basic type' as a working hypothesis (see chapter 9). This 'basic type' has the same meaning as Marsh's 'baramin', 'Genesis kind', 'archetype' etc.

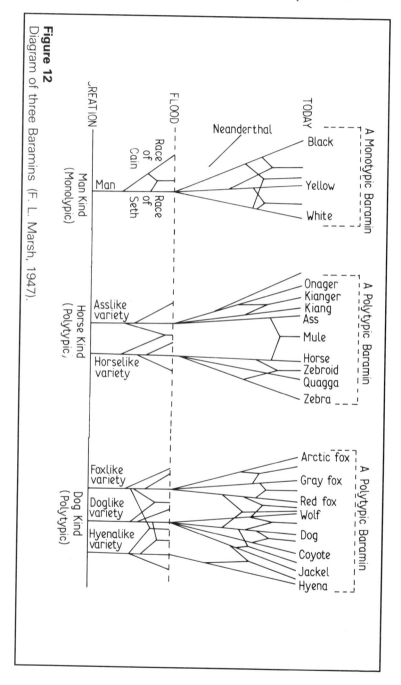

Figure 12
Diagram of three Baramins (F. L. Marsh, 1947).

Conclusion

Discontinuity seems to be characteristic of nature, and this conflicts with the essential concept of evolutionary theory that all organisms can be traced back to a common ancestor, some prehistoric amoeba. Evolution, therefore, has to explain

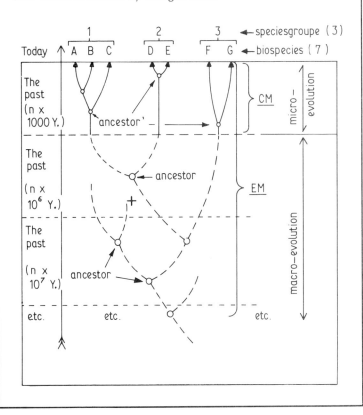

Figure 13
Difference in explanations concerning the origin of species between the CM (creation model) and EM (evolution model). A group of species corresponds with the Genesis kind and can be compared with a present systematic Family like, for instance, the Mammals.
'n' is between the numbers 1 and 10.
Relationships indicated by a dotted line are more hypothetical than those indicated by straight lines.

discontinuity in terms of divergent archetypes. The difference between the creation and evolution models can therefore be represented as shown in Figure 13. In the creation model the archetypal age is no more than a few thousand years, whereas in evolutionary thinking it goes back thousands of millions of years. To give the overall creation model, Figures 12 and 13 should be taken together.

Micro-evolution is nothing other than the dynamic response of species to the environment, and must not be confused with or extrapolated to a speculative process of macro-evolution which by definition cannot be observed scientifically. Of course, the creationist concept of a Creator is also incapable of being tested scientifically. But there are other insights, including those of modern information theory, which suggest that life could never have arisen by chance. That is another story, but it supports the rationality of the creationist position.

Bibliography

Ager, D.V., (1956), 'Geographical factors in fossil species', in *The species concept in palaeontology*, a symposium ed. Sylvester-Bradley, P.C., (The Syst. Assn., London, 1956).

Bumpus, A.C., (1896), in Emmel, T.C., *Population Biology*, 1976, p.56.

Carlquist, S., (1965), 'Island Life' in Emmel, T.C., *op.cit.*

Croze, H., (1970), *Searching image in carrion crows*, Z. Tierpsychol, suppl.5.

Dobzhansky, T., (1951), *Genetics and the Origin of Species*, (New York, Columbia University Press).

Ehrman, L., Spassky, B., Pavlovsky, O., Dobshanzky, Th., (1965), *Sexual selection, geotaxis and chromosomal polymorfism in experimental populations of Drosophila pseudoobscura*, (Evolution, Lancaster, Pa.) 19: 337-346.

Emmel, T.C., (1976), *Population Biology*, (Harper & Row, New York).

Harper, G.H., (1981), 'Speciation or Irruption: The significance of the Darwin finches', (*Creation Research Society Quarterly* reprint 1980 of article in *Journal of Biological Education*, vol.14, no.2, pp.99-106).

Hooykaas, R., (1976), *Geschiedenis der natuurwetenschappen*, 2nd ed., (Utrecht, Bohn, Scheltema & Holkema).

Kettlewell, H.B.D., (1973), *The evolution of Melanism*, (Oxford University Press).

Krebs, C.J., (1972), *Ecology*, (Harper & Row, New York).

Kreutzer, H.H., Oskamp, A.A.G., (1975), *Biologie* (4,5) (Wolters-Noordhoff, Groningen).

Marsh, F.L., (1947), *Evolution, Creation and Science*, 2nd ed., (Review and Herald Publishing Association, Washington).

Marsh, F.L., (1950), *Studies in Creationism*, (Review and Herald Publishing Association, Washington).

Marsh, F.L., (1966), *De Schepping van de Soorten*, (De Stem der Leken, The Hague), (original title: *Life, Man and Time*, 1966).

Mayr, E., (1963), *Animal species and Evolution*, (Cambridge).

Mettler, L.E., Gregg, T.G., (1969), *Population Genetics and Evolution*, (Prentice-Hall, Englewood Cliffs).

Origin of Species (1981), British Museum (Natural History), (Cambridge University Press).

Ouweneel, W.J., (1976), *De Ark in de branding*, (Buijten & Schipperheijn, Amsterdam).

Petit, C., (1958), *La determinisme génétique et psycho-physiologique de la competition sexuelle chez D. melanogaster*, (Bull. Biol. Fr. Belg. 92:248-329).

Sevenster, P., (1973), 'De rol van leerprocessen in natuurlijke situaties' in *Ethologie, de biologie van gedrag*, (Centr. v. Landb. publ., Wageningen) pp.205-222.

Sirks, M.J., 'De variabiliteit van het soortsbegrip', *1949 Yearbook of Biology*, Dodonaea 16, pp.176-194, taken from the lecture notes of the Department of Plant Taxonomy of the Free University of Amsterdam, 1975.

Solbrig, O.T., 1970, *Principles and Methods in Plant Biosystematics* (London).

Thompson, E.Y., *et. al.*, (1911) in Emmel, T.C., *op. cit.*, p.56.

Tinbergen, N., (1978), *In't vrije veld* (Aula 611, Het Spectrum, Utrecht/Antwerp) (translation of *Curious Naturalists* (1958, 1974), (Penguin Education, Harmondsworth, Middlesex, England).

Vakgroep plantensystematiek (1975) (Lecture notes of the Department of Plant Taxonomy, Free University of Amsterdam).

8.

Possibilities and limitations of improvement by random changes to textual data

Eberhard Bertsch

Summary

We discuss the effects of random alterations of character strings. In computer science, character strings occur as parameters of procedures and as actual representations of procedures.[1] It is shown that changes of parameters will generally lead to modified versions of previously existing data. On the other hand, changes of procedure representations will almost always destroy the original meaning. There is no evidence that new concepts of computing can be expected as the result of an arbitary amount of random changes in any realistic time span.

These observations are compared with analogous ones in molecular genetics. In particular, a well-known microbial regulatory mechanism is considered.[2] We conclude that random changes lack the properties required for a source of essentially new, meaningful information. The paper is written with as little mathematical notation as possible.

1. Introduction

Every method of information transmission encountered in the physical world is subject to a certain amount of erroneous processing.[3] Leaving aside intentional distortions of messages, the causes of errors may be traced to faulty material, lack of some resource, or various kinds of unforeseen interference. Human hastiness or fatigue may be regarded as special cases of interference.

In principle, a given text that is used to convey some meaning may or may not be changed accidentally in the course of time. If it is, the question may be raised whether the resulting text is also meaningful, and if so, in what ways the meaning of the new text differs from that of the old one.

In a simple diagram, the above possibility can be sketched as follows:

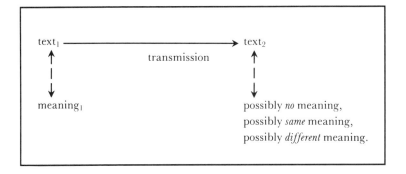

To be somewhat more precise, we must explain the notion of 'meaning'.[4]

In general linguistics and in computer science, the set of all character sequences over a given alphabet is generally divided into two disjoint subsets: the set of those sequences that are syntactically correct, and the set of those that are not.

On the set of correct sequences, a function *Sem* is defined which associates a unique sequence of elementary computer operations or some other object with each correct character sequence. The object associated with a given character string is called its *meaning*.

People who are unfamiliar with mathematical terminology are often surprised to learn that the previous concepts are entirely general. In other words they do not presuppose any more specific properties of languages.[5]

For example, if the alphabet consists only of the letters a, b and c and the syntax consists of the single rule: 'Two adjacent symbols must not be the same', then

abc, baba, cabc

are syntactically correct, while

aab, baab, cacc

are not.

A second example is that of a computer programming language (e.g. Pascal). Such a language also has rules of syntax, so that the statement

'If O *then* a *then* b'

is syntactically incorrect and thus meaningless whereas the statement

'*if* a > O *then* b := a'

is correct and has the obvious operational meaning[6] which is 'understood' by the computer programme.

2. Random changes

All textual changes can be seen as consisting conceptually of certain elementary changes in a given combination. In principle, the two operations *deletion* and *insertion* of elements can be combined to produce changes of arbitrary complexity.[7]

To be somewhat more realistic, *transitions* and *transpositions* should also be considered as elementary. A transition exchanges an arbitrary character for a different one in the same position. A transposition swaps two adjacent characters. As we try to refrain from formal definitions (for the benefit of the uninitiated reader), we give one example for each of the elementary changes mentioned so far.

Suppose the original string is the name of the town where this conference is being held.

'Heverlee'.

Applying $\left\{\begin{array}{ll} \text{a deletion,} & \text{'Hevrlee'} \\ \text{an insertion,} & \text{'Heveerlee'} \\ \text{a transition,} & \text{'Hevarlee'} \\ \text{a transposition,} & \text{'Hevrelce'} \end{array}\right\}$ results

For computer scientists, it is immediately clear that most accidental changes (errors) of textual data are of an elementary nature in the sense just discussed.

From what is known in molecular biology, we may assert that the same holds for genetic mutations. A particularly simple type of mutation occurs when a certain amount of 2-aminopurine is available at the time of gene duplication.[8]

The structural similarity of that substance to both adenine and guanine leads to its coupling with their respective counterparts. (Structurally, adenine is 6-aminopurine, and guanine is 2-amino-6-hydroxypurine.) This leads to the following possible base pairs in the presence of 2AP:

$\updownarrow$
A	T	C	G	2AP	T	2AP	C
T	A	G	C	T	2AP	C	2AP

Example:

A DNA base sequence
 ... A T T G C A C C G A T ...
yields the counterpart sequence in the normal course of events (no 2AP present).
 ... T A A C G T G G C T A ....
If 2AP is available at the next cycle of duplication, one such molecule may couple with, say, the central T, giving the sequence
 ... A T T G C *M* C C G A T ...
where the letter *M* represents one molecule of 2AP.

At the next cycle, M may couple with T. In that case, the harmful effect has been undone again, since the original sequence is recovered.

It may, however, couple with C, yielding
... T A A C G C G G C T A ....
Now the gene containing that sequence is a mutant of the
previous one.

3. Changes of parametric data

'Parametric data' are sequences of characters that are
passively employed in the process of computation. They
constitute the information *on which* certain operations are to be
performed. In contrast, 'procedure representations' describe
how and in *what order* operations are to be executed.[9] Quite
obviously, random changes of parametric data will produce
syntactically incorrect strings in many cases.

Thus, if the number 4711 is changed into 471a, 47?1, ***, or
4(1), it is no longer a legitimate number.

However, if the new string is 4712, 4721, or 5711, it
expresses meaningful new information. Under certain circumstances, the new number will be meaningless in a larger
context; but it is not unrealistic to assume that unintentional
replacement of numbers will sometimes produce equally
useful or even more useful information. The latter possibility
will exist when there is a range of viable values, within which
the current optimum is determined by external factors.
Random changes may approximate that optimum.

To give an example, in numerical process-control the initial
value of a physical quantity may have been prescribed in a
way that is suboptimal under certain conditions.[10]

If that is so, and if the conditions in question arise, random
changes may lead to an improvement of process efficiency.

This is an important point, because it helps to demonstrate
and define the concept of variability *within* a predetermined
framework. Under the above assumptions, there will be no
change in the way the programme works. The algorithm will
remain essentially the same, and, furthermore, nothing has
occurred that would tend to create a different algorithm.[9]

In terms of genetics, a new mutant allele will have been
added to the gene pool.[11]

With non-numeric parametric data, the above is less

evident, but still valid. Let us consider the frequent example of unintentional address changes.

The original address may be

> Fritz Förster
> Waldstraße 21
> 5999 Kleinholzdorf.

Again, if the numerical *parts* of that string are changed, there is a slight chance of useful new meaning.

If 21 becomes 29 and another man with the same name happens to live at that address, the (incorrect) delivery of some advertisement may turn out to be useful.

If 5999 becomes 4999, if that postal code exists, and if the name of the corresponding village is also Kleinholzdorf, the letter or package will be incorrectly delivered. (It will probably be forwarded to the correct address later on, since the postal service will be aware of the ambiguous village name.)

Changes of alphabetical characters will normally be taken for what they are, namely typing errors. There are some sensitive spots, however. Suppose 'Fritz' becomes 'Franz' and a person with that name lives at the same address. Then he may get the letter and may have some use for it.

By using the imagination, various other useful changes of passive data can be found. It should be kept in mind, however, that such changes do not affect the description of the mode of control in the computer.

4. Changes of 'procedure representations'

When the descriptions of algorithms are subjected to random changes, the situation is entirely different. As a general observation over many years of programming practice, such changed programmes either fail to run, or break down immediately, or get into infinite loops (doing the same operations over and over again), or do only part of the job.[12] There is no indication that random changes will produce anything resembling a new concept or programme. We have investigated in detail various changes of existing sorting and searching procedures.[13]

The procedure that we present below is probably the

simplest imaginable method of searching for a given element in an array of numbers.[14] Let us consider the effects of providing a series of independent textual changes. Short descriptions will be given of the result in each case.

We use the programming language PASCAL.[15] The necessary declarations of items are omitted. Suppose L is an array with components indexed from 1 to n where n>1.

1. j := 1; (let the variable 'j' equal one)

2. while (j<=n) and L[j]<>X) do (continue the search operation until the element sought is found)

3. j := j+1; (increment j by one)

4. if j>n then j := 0; etcetera.

We consider all occurrences of the terms j, n, 1, 0 and examine the effect of replacing such an occurrence by some other term.

n := 1 in line 1 makes j undefined. The search will check no more than the first element of the array.
1 := 1 or 0 := 1 are syntactically incorrect.
j := j leaves j undefined. The search may check only part or none of the array elements.
j := n entails that only the last element is checked.
j := 0 introduces an invalid element. In general this will have no effect. Some compilers may reject this statement.
n <= n in line 2 will lead to a search in invalid parts of storage. The same happens with 0 <= n and 1 <= n and j <= j.
j <= 1 or j <= 0 restrict the search to the first element or none at all, respectively.
L[n] entails that the element is only found if it is equal to the last element of the array.
L[1] does the same with the first element.
L[0] accesses invalid data.
0 := or 1 := in line 3 are invalid.
n := j+1 produces an infinite loop, as j is never increased.
Likewise j := 0+1 or j := 1+1 lead to infinite loops.

j := n+1 terminates the search after the first comparison.
j := j+0 produces an infinite loop.
j := j+n leads to termination after the first comparison.
j := j+j skips many elements of the array, excepting only those at a position that is a power of two.
n>n or j>j in line 4 is never true. Thus the case when the element has not been found is handled improperly.
The same happens when 1>n or 0>n are there instead.
j>1 or j>0 have the effect that j := 0 is always executed. Thus it appears as if the element had not been found even if it has.
n := 0 in line 4 instead of j := 0 fails to distinguish the case when the element has not been found. 0 := 0 or 1 := 0 are syntactically wrong.
Finally j := n, j := 1 give the incorrect impression that an element that is not there has been found, and j := j makes line 4 useless.

We now apply these ideas, by analogy, to a particular genetic process.

5. Changes of the lactose operon of the bacterium Escherichia coli

The following diagram sketches the function of the lactose operon of coli bacteria.[16]

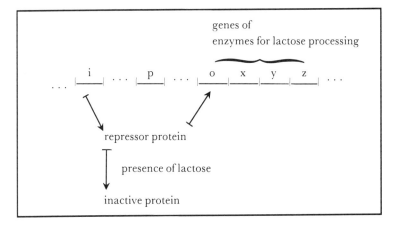

In non-mutated bacteria, a gene *i* codes for a protein that becomes attached to a particular site *o* on the genome whenever there is no lactose around. This attachment prevents RNA-polymerase molecules, attached to site p, from moving across o and transcribing the x, y and z genes into messenger RNA for the enzymes ß-galactosidase, permease and transacetylase.[17]

As soon as there is a sufficient amount of lactose available, the repressor protein molecules become inactive by linkage with individual lactose molecules. Thus the repressors can no longer occupy *o*, the RNA-polymerase can start its activity and the enzymes needed for lactose processing are synthesized. When there is no lactose left, the repressor returns to its binding site on *o*, and the system returns to a quiescent state.

Let us now consider some of the known mutants of participating genes.

There is a mutant of *i*, called *i–*, that prevents the synthesis of repressors.

Thus the enzymes are *always* produced, no matter whether there is lactose around.

Another mutant of *i*, called i^s, produces a repressor that cannot be inactivated.

Thus there is no synthesis of enzymes.

A mutant of *o*, called o^c, has an ineffective binding site for the repressor. Consequently, the enzymes are *always* produced.

The mutant o^o keeps the polymerase from starting. There are thus no enzymes.

In addition, there are some mutants of x, y and z that make the enzymes themselves ineffective. In that case, lactose cannot be processed.

We may summarize this by saying that the described mutants of the E. coli lac-operon are all defective in some way or other. None of them offers an advantageous tendency towards a different regulatory mechanism. In our previous terminology, the lac genes exist to control the mode of processing. They are not passive parametric data.

From our discussion of programming languages, we would expect that changes of the lac operon would not lead to essential improvement. Our expectation has been confirmed by the available experimental data.

6. Conclusion

Random changes of textual data may lead to improvement if the data represent a particular choice within a certain range of elementary possibilities. This phenomenon seems to account for various known cases of variability in technology and nature.[18]

On the other hand, data constituting the description of a *process* are destroyed by random changes. There can be no hope that computer science will obtain new discoveries by subjecting existing programmes to arbitrary sequences of blind modifications. By analogy, the same may be assumed to hold in nature.[19]

Bibliography

1. S. Baase, *Computer Algorithms: Introduction to Design and Analysis*, Addison-Wesley Publ. Comp. Reading, Massachusetts (1978).
2. L. Träger, *Einführung in die Molekularbiologie*, VEB G. Fischer, Jena (1975).
3. E. Henze, H.H. Homuth, *Einführung in die Informationstheorie*, Vieweg, Braunschweig (1970).
4. N. Chomsky, *Aspects of the Theory of Syntax*, M.I.T. Press, Cambridge, Massachusetts (1965).
5. N. Chomsky, M.P. Schützenberger, 'The Algebric Theory of Context-free Languages' in *Computer Programming and Formal Systems*. North Holland, Amsterdam (1963).
6. N. Wirth, *The Programming Language PASCAL*, Acta Informatica 1 (1971), 35 ff.
7. J.P. Levy, *Automatic Correction of Syntax Errors in Programming Languages*, Acta Informatica 4 (1975), 271 ff.
8. L. Träger, *op. cit.*
9. S. Baase, *op. cit.*
10. W. Werum, H. Windauer, *PEARL, Process and Experiment Automation Realtime Language*, Vieweg, Braunschweig (1978).
11. L. Träger, *op. cit.*
12. M.P. Schützenberger, 'Algorithms and the Neo-Darwinian Theory of Evolution,' in: *Mathematical Challenges to the Neo-Darwinian Interpretation of Evolution*. Wistar Institute for Anatomy and Physiology, Philadelphia (1967).

13. E. Bertsch, 'Mutationen aus der Sicht der Informatik,' in: *Struktur und Information in Technik und Natur,* Bericht ATWD-18 der Phys.-Techn. Bundesanstalt. Reproduced in W. Gitt (ed.): *Am Anfang war die Information,* Resch-Verlag, Gräfelfing (1982).
14. S. Baase, *op. cit.*
15. N. Wirth, *op. cit.*
16. Y. Oshima, M. Matsuura, T. Horiuchi, *Conformational Change of the lac repressor induced with the inducer.* Biochem. Biophys. Res.Com. 47 (1972), 1444 ff.
17. W.S. Reznikoff, J.H. Miller, J.G. Scaife, J.R. Beckwith, *A mechanism for repressor action.* J. Mol. Biol.43 (1968), 201 ff.
18. F.L. Marsh, *Variation and Fixity in Nature.* Creation Research Society Books, Norcross, Georgia (1982).
19. A.E. Wilder Smith, *The Creation of Life — A Cybernetic Approach to Evolution,* Shaw Publ., Wheaton, Illinois (1970).

9.

On the limits of variability: evidence and speculation from morphology, genetics and molecular biology

Siegfried Scherer

Creationism is not a science

It is the aim of all evolutionary thinking to demonstrate the non-limited variability of life. The variability of domesticated animals and plants led Charles Darwin to postulate the evolutionary 'origin of species by means of natural selection'.

Participants in this conference are aware of the philosophical assumption which, in fact, forms the basis of evolutionary thinking. However, we should also agree on the basic religious assumption which leads us as creationists to postulate the limited variability of life. To clarify this position I would like to summarize this as a basic statement: *'Life has been created in entities called 'kinds' which propagate descendants belonging to the same basic type.'*

This assumption is purely religious. Thus creationism can never be science, just as evolution cannot be science. However, the assumptions of evolutionists and creationists raise several questions which may be investigated by means of natural science. In this paper I would like to address the following questions resulting from the creationist assumption:

1. Is it possible to demonstrate these 'kinds' in biology?
2. Is it possible to demonstrate conclusively that the variability of living things is limited?

The following, however, should be made clear. The questions arising from our basic assumption can be tested by science even though the assumption itself cannot be.

We may or may not find a valuable scientific answer, of course. If we find one, our basic assumption is by no means verified! The only conclusion to be drawn in this case is that our assumption does not contradict the natural sciences.

From these remarks it should be evident that the creationist position which I am taking in this paper cannot be proven or disproven in a scientific sense, just as evolution cannot be proven. It is therefore not 'natural science'. However, the bulk of the following arguments is based on morphology, genetics and molecular biology and thus I attempt to support my creationist position by facts originating from natural sciences. Please note that the same is true for evolutionary thinking! Thus creationism and evolutionism share a sort of 'hybridization' between natural sciences and philosophy. To quote Andrews (1984): 'Creationism is an holistic philosophy which seeks to understand the scientific enterprise within a biblical and theological framework. In pursuing this concept and rejecting the arid materialism which underlies so much modern thinking we are simply returning to the paradigm espoused by such as Newton, Boyle, Kelvin, Faraday and Maxwell, who among others laid the foundations of science as we know it.'

What is a kind?

To my knowledge it was the biologist F.L. Marsh (1947; 1976) who first tried to give an answer to the fundamental question of what a 'kind' actually is. He suggested labelling the biblical kind 'baramin' or 'basic type', summarizing under this systematic category all animals and plants which show the same overall morphology and may — at least in principle — produce hybrids. As will be shown later, this systematic category has no connection with the 'biospecies' defined by Mayr (1966), based on the observations of micro-evolutionary processes. In this paper the following definition will be used: *'Belonging to the same "basic type" are all organisms among which hybrids occur or whose germ-cells can perform true fertilization (that is,*

Figure 1 *Aix galericulata* (Mandarin Duck, Mandarinente). This duck is a member of the heterogenous tribe Cairinini. It is the most colourful of the 149 species of the Anatidae. Breeding habitats are river valleys with wooded islands, forest lakelets with willow-lined banks or small forest ponds in East China. Their foods are quite variable (insects, snails, plants etc). Photograph by S. Scherer.

Figure 2 *Cygnus melanocoryphus* (Black-necked Swan, Schwarzhalsschwan). This rather small swan (body weight up to 5 kg) is a member of the tribe Anserini, consisting of swans and geese. *Cygnus melanocoryphus* lives on fresh-water and brackish-water marshes of South America and eats mainly plant materials. Photograph by R. Wiskin, Switzerland.

Figure 3 *Cereopsis novae-hollandiae* (Cape Barren Goose, Hühnergans). This bird forms a tribe with only one monotypic species and is considered to be an 'aberrant type'. It lives on various small islands in the South of Australia, inhabiting open areas such as beaches and grassy areas. It generally avoids entering water. About two-thirds of all its food is composed of grasses. *Cereopsis* forms flocks of up to 300 individuals. Photograph by S. Scherer.

Figure 4 Hybrid between *Somateria mollissima* (Common Eider, Eiderente) and *Tadorna tadorna* (Northern Shelduck, Brandgans), living in the zoo of Basel, Switzerland. It has been described by Wackernagel (1972). Most interestingly, two only distantly related tribes (Mergini, Seaducks and Tadornini, Shelducks) are connected by this hybrid. No progenitors have been observed in Basel. Photograph by S. Scherer.

the initiation of embryonic development with the genes of both parents being expressed), or which are connected indirectly by hybridization.'

Until now, as far as I know, no taxonomy has been worked out using this concept. The attempts to define basic types in biology have been rather superficial, so that I felt it necessary to test Marsh's approach in detail using the avian family of the Anatidae. The work reported here has been published elsewhere in greater detail (Scherer & Hilsberg 1982, Scherer & Sontag 1986). The reader is referred to this literature for further information. Independently, Siegler (1976; 1978) assumed speculatively that the Anatidae constitute a basic type.

Ducks, swans and geese: using a special example

The order of the Anseriformes comprises today two families of birds: firstly the Anhimidae, more chicken-like birds, consisting of only three species, and secondly the Anatidae. These two families are morphologically well separated. The family Anatidae is characterized mainly by a typical duck-like bill covered by a sensitive skin and equipped with special lamellae (Figs. 1-4, also shown in colour on front cover). Commonly we distinguish between ducks, swans and geese. However, the new taxonomy according to Johnsgard (1978) prefers the classification into two sub-families, Anseranatinae (with only one monotypic species, the Magpie Goose *Anseranas semipalmata*) and the Anserinae (12 tribes with 148 species). Occasionally, *Anseranas* is regarded as comprising a unique family apart from the Anatidae (e.g. Woolfenden, 1961; Scherer & Sontag, 1985).

The Anatidae form a quite heterogenous group of birds (see Figs. 1-4), ranging from the small *Aix* (400-500g) to the large *Cygnus* (up to 12000g). But apart from *Anseranas*, there is no doubt from a morphological and anatomical point of view that all 148 species belong to the Anatidae. By contrast, however, the classification of the species within the Anatidae is less clear and a variety of intra-anatidal classifications do exist. For example, some aberrant types comprise features of several different tribes (e.g. *Thalassornis, Coscoroba, Plectropterus* and others). In Figure 4 *Cereopsis novae-hollandiae* is shown, a monotypic species belonging to the tribe Cereopsini. This aberrant duck incorporates features of the Tadornini, Anserini and Anatini, three completely different tribes of the Anatidae. Special bill forms or particular patterns of plumage are seemingly widespread among several tribes. Thus the intra-anatidal classification is fraught with difficulties in some cases.

However, these features seem to be explicable in a creationist model of origins. The characteristics of the created,

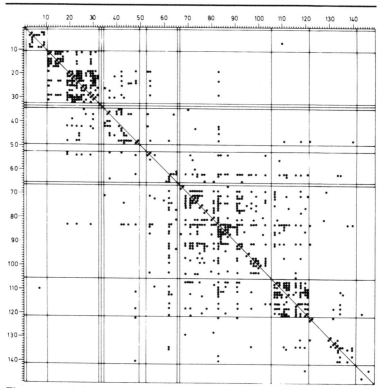

Figure 5 Crossbreeding matrix of the Anatidae (reprinted from Scherer and Hilsberg 1982). The numbers represent the 149 species of the Anatidae, given in detail in the original paper, and belong to the following tribes: 1 Anseranatini; 2-10 Dendrocygnini; 11-32 Anserini; 33 Cereopsini; 34 Stictonettini; 35-49 Tadornini; 50-52 Tachyerini; 53-65 Cairinini; 66 Merganettini; 67-105 Anatini; 106-121 Aythyini; 122-141 Mergini; 142-149 Oxyurini.

ancient form could have become divided (by chance or by controlled genetic processes) into diverse, seemingly 'independent' constellations through micro-evolutionary processes, leading to the various biospecies known today. The alternative (evolutionary) explanation of convergence is not adequate for these cases, as no selective pressure has been recognized which could lead to the evolution of such distinct forms.

It is not widely known that a variety of different species are in fact able to cross-breed. In natural habitats this process is rare — the 'biological' species seem to be rather stable. If cross-breeding does occur frequently, the taxonomist has difficulty in defining the taxonomic status of the species/races involved. Mayr (1969) suggested the term 'superspecies' for these cases.

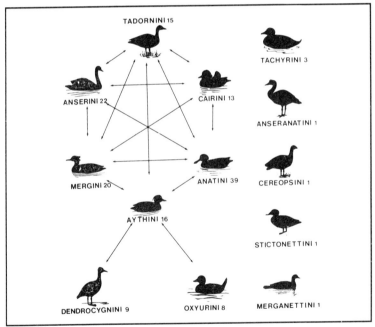

Figure 6 Most tribes of the Anatidae are connected by hybridization. According to Johnsgard (1978) the Anatidae contain 13 tribes with 149 species. The numbers given after the tribes represent the number of species. From each tribe a typical species is given in contours. On the right part of the figure the aberrant tribes are mentioned. Drawing by T. Hilsberg.

From the literature I have collected 418 interspecific, intergeneric and intertribal hybrids (Fig. 5). Accordingly, 126 out of 149 species of the Anatidae are therefore connected directly or indirectly through hybridization (Fig. 6). In Figure 4 a hybrid between completely different tribes (Tadornini and Mergini) is shown. Normally no hybrids are known among the aberrant types mentioned earlier, meaning in many cases that no one has attempted a cross. However, in some cases it seems that no hybridization is possible — even between two species of the same genus.

Generally, interspecific hybrids are fertile, whereas many of the intertribal hybrids are sterile (Table 1). The absolute percentage of fertility is not known due to the lack of

	Fertile hybrids observed			
	Total	interspecific	intergeneric	intertribal
Number	90	59	18	13
%	100	65	20	15

Table 1: Fertility of hybrids between different anatidal species. 418 hybrids were collected from the literature (see Fig. 5). Of these, 90 are known to be fertile, some are known to be sterile and in most cases no detailed investigation had been performed.

experiments. In addition the commencement of embryonic development has not been investigated in most of the species reported on in the literature. Thus, fertility of the hybrids does not seem to provide a useful tool for taxonomy.

It is important to mention that no hybrids between anatidal and other birds are known (Gray, 1958). Thus, the definition given above provides a clear-cut systematic marker for the Anatidae.

Most interesting is the morphology of the hybrids. I have collected eleven crossings where the hybrid does not resemble its parents but rather another anatidal species, sometimes living on a different continent (Table 2). The same is found for ethology. We may interpret these findings by speculating that a created basic type split up into different biological species. The basic genetic information would remain *very similar* in these species, and the genetic constellation becomes easily disturbed by hybridization, leading to the phenomena mentioned above.

Parental species	Hybrid similar to:
Aythya fuligula x *A ferina*	*Aythya affinis*
A. fuligula x *A. nyroca*	*A. baeri*
A. fuligula x *A. marila*	*A. affinis*
A. valisneria x *A. americana*	*A. ferina*
Anser anser x *Branta canadensis*	*Anser c. caerulescens*
Anas clypeata x *Anas crecca*	*A. formosa*
A. clypeata x *A. penelope*	*A. formosa*
A. clypeata x *A. cyanoptera*	*A. rhynchotis*
A. acuta x *A. crecca*	*A. formosa*
A. penelope x *A. silibatrix*	*A. americana*

Table 2: Similarities of hybrids with other than the parental species. Reprinted from Scherer & Hilsberg 1982, see this publication for literature and pictures.

Molecular taxonomy of the Anatidae

There is little information about the molecular systematics of birds. I have collected and summarized the information available for the Anatidae (Scherer & Sontag, 1986). Concerning (a) the amino acid composition or electrophoretic mobility of proteins, (b) the composition of waxes of the uropygial gland and (c) lysozyme sequences, it is quite clear that the Anatidae are clearly distinguished from all other bird families. However, it is difficult to work out an intra-family systematic based on these characters. To use an example, two lysozymes are found among the Anatidae, goose-type lysozyme in some species and chicken-type lysozyme in others. Some species have both types of proteins or another kind of lysozyme difficult to integrate into the system. However, the occurrence of the lysozyme in no way correlates with the taxonomic position of the species investigated (Bailey *et. al.*, 1976; Scherer & Sontag, 1986). From the creationist point of view, one may again speculate on a created basic type, perhaps possessing both types of lysozymes. In the course of speciation, genes have been lost or slightly changed by chance, producing the puzzling picture of the Anatidae.

Using amino-acid sequences of haemoglobin we have calculated dendrograms (Fig. 7). On the basis of the α-haemoglobins the Anatidae are well separated from the other orders of birds but β-haemoglobins (not shown) allow no reasonable classification of the Anatidae. Note that neither α-haemoglobins nor β-haemoglobins (Scherer & Sontag 1986) produce reasonable phylogenetic trees in evolutionary terms. For instance, the Rheidae and Struthionidae should be grouped together (order: Struthioniformes) and separate from the other birds investigated, being considered a 'primitive group' (Harrison 1978, Kuhn 1971), yet Figure 7 shows they are not. Again, the Phoenicopteriformes (Flamingos) are considered to be the nearest relatives to the Anseriformes (Harrison 1978, Wolters 1975-82, but see also Milner 1981). However, compared with the Anatidae, *Phoenicopterus* has the most different α-haemoglobin.

It is not unusual for dendrograms, constructed by means of amino-acid sequences, not to fit the palaeontological and morphological evidence (see for example Baba *et. al.* 1981 for cytochromes, Scherer & Sontag 1983 for ferredoxins, Schwabe 1984 for relaxin and Scherer *et. al.* 1985 for plastocyanin and cytochrome-c-553).

The basic type: a useful working hypothesis?

Based on these data I suggest that the species of the Anatidae (except *Anseranas semipalmata*) belong to one basic type. Thus all anatidal species *may be* connected by historical, phylogenetic relationships. It is my contention that the limits of variability are determined by the limits of the basic type.

If this concept is to be really useful it has to be applicable to other groups of organisms. Without going into detail I should

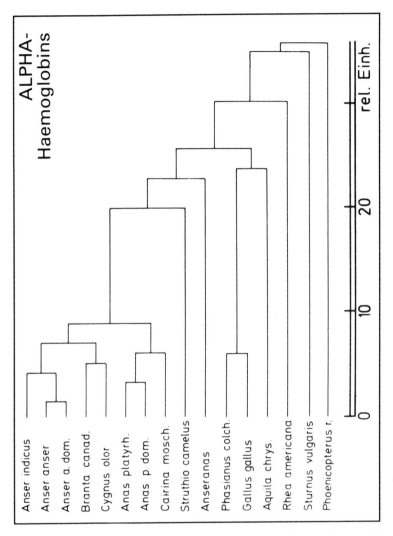

Figure 7 Dendrogram constructed from the amino-acid sequences of alpha haemoglobins from different birds (for detailed literature see Scherer & Sontag 1986. The difference matrix was calculated according to Fitch & Margoliash (1967). For the dendrogram construction a Digital pdp-11 computer, Galway, Ireland was used, with a weighted average linkage programme (Steinhausen & Langer 1977). The distance between the species is expressed in relative units. Please note that other algorithms may result in different dendograms!

Figure 8

	Key	1	11	21	31
(1)	ANS.IND	VLSAADKTNV	KGVFSKISGH	AQQYGAQTLQ	RMFTAYPETK
(2)	ANS.ANS	VLSAADKTNV	KGVFSKIGGH	AQQYGAQTLQ	RMFTAYPETK
(3)	ANS.A.DO	VLSAADKTNV	KGVFSKIGGH	AQQYGAQTLQ	RMFTAYPETK
(4)	BR.CAN	VLSAADKTNV	KGVFSKIGGH	ADQYGAQTLQ	RMFVAYPETK
(5)	CYGN.O	VLSAADKTNV	KGVFSKIGGH	ADDYGAQTLQ	RMFIAYPETK
(6)	ANA.P.P	VLSAADKTNV	KGVFSKIGGH	AQQYGAQTLQ	RMFIAYPETK
(7)	ANA.P.DO	VLSAADKANV	KGVFSKIGGH	AQQYGAQTLQ	RMFIAYPETK
(8)	C.MOSCH	VLSAADKTNV	KGVFSKIGGH	AQQYGAQTLQ	RMFIAYPETK
(9)	ANS.SEM	VLSAADKGNV	KTVFGKIGGH	AQQYGAQTLE	RMFETFPETK
(10)	STR.CAM	VLSGTDKTNV	KGIFSKISSH	AQQYGAQTLQ	RMFITYPETK
(11)	RHEA.AM	VLSGPDKTNV	KNVFAKIGGH	ADAYGAQTLQ	RMFITYPETK
(12)	PHAS.COL	VLSAADKNNV	KGIFTKIAGH	AQQYGAQALQ	RMFITYPSTK
(13)	GALLUS	VLSAADKNNV	KGIFTKIAGH	AQQYGAQTLQ	RMFITYPPTK
(14)	AQU.CH	VLSANDKTNV	KNVFTKISGH	AQDYGAQALQ	RMFITYPPTK

		41	51	61	71
(1)	ANS.IND	TYFPHFDLEH	GSAEIKAHGK	KVVAALVQAV	NHIDDIAGAL
(2)	ANS.ANS	TYFPHFDLEH	GSAEIKAHGK	KVAAALVQAV	NHIDDIAGAL
(3)	ANS.A.DO	TYFPHFDLEH	GSAEIKAHGK	KVAAALVQAV	NHIDDIAGAL
(4)	BR.CAN	TYFPHFDLEH	GSAEIKAHGK	KVAAALVQAV	NHIDDIAGAL
(5)	CYGN.0	TYFPHFDLEH	GSAEIKAHGK	KVAAALVQAV	NHIDDIAGAL
(6)	ANA.P.P	TYFPHFDLSH	GSAEIKAHGK	KVAAALVQAV	NHIDDIAGAL
(7)	ANA.P.DO	TYFPHFDLSH	GSAEIKAHGK	KVAAALVQAV	NHVDDIAGAL
(8)	C.MOSCH	TTFPHFDLEH	GSAEIKAHGK	KVAAALVQAV	NHIDDIAGAL
(9)	ANS.SEM	TYFPHFDLEP	GSAEIKAHGK	KVAAALVQAA	NHIDDIAGAL
(10)	STR.CAM	TYFPHFDLHH	GSAEIKAHGK	KVANALIQAV	NHIDDISGAL
(11)	RHEA.AM	TYFPHFDLHH	GSAEIKTHGK	KVVSALIDAA	NHIDDIYGAL
(12)	PHAS.COL	TYFPHFDLSH	GSAEIKGHGK	KVVAALIQAV	NHIDDITGTL
(13)	GALLUS	TYFPHFDLSH	GSAEIKGHGK	KVVAALIQAA	NHIDDIAGTL
(14)	AQU.CH	TYFPHFDLHH	GSAEIKAHGK	KVVGALIQAV	NHIDDMAGAL

		81	91	101	111
(1)	ANS.IND	SKLSDLHAEK	LRVDPVNFKF	LGHCFLVVVA	IHHPSALTAQ
(2)	ANS.ANS	SKLSDLHAEK	LRVDPVNFKF	LGHCFLVVVA	IHHPSALTPQ
(3)	ANS.A.DO	SKLSDLHAEK	LRVDPVNFKF	LGHCFLVVVA	IHHPSALTPQ
(4)	BR.CAN	SKLSDLHAEK	LRVDPVNFKF	LGHCFLVVVA	IHHPSALTPQ
(5)	CYGN.0	SKLSDLHAEK	LRVDPVNFKF	LGHCFLVVVA	IHHPSALTPQ
(6)	ANA.P.P	SKLSDLHAEK	LRVDPVNFKF	LGHCFLVVVA	IHHPAALTPQ
(7)	ANA.P.DO	SKLSDLHAEK	LRVDPVNFKF	LGHCFLVVVA	IHHPAALTPQ
(8)	C.MOSCH	SKLSDLHAEK	LRVDPVNFKF	LGHCFLVVLA	IHHPAALTPQ
(9)	ANS.SEM	SKLSDLHAEK	LRVDPVNFKF	LGHCFLVVVA	IHHPSLLTPQ
(10)	STR.CAM	SKLSDLHAEK	LRVDPVNFKL	LGECFLVVVA	IHHPSLLTPQ
(11)	RHEA.AM	SKLSDLHAEK	LRVDPVNFKL	LGECFLVVVA	IHHPSALTPQ
(12)	PHAS.COL	SKLSDLHAHK	LRVDPVNFKL	LGECFLVVVA	IHHPSALTPQ
(13)	GALLUS	SKLSDLHAHK	LRVDPVNFKL	LGECFLVVVA	IHHPAALTPQ
(14)	AQU.CH	SKLSDLHAEK	LRVDPVNFKL	LGECFLVVVA	IHHPSVLTPQ

		121	131
(1)	ANS.IND	VHASLDKFLC	AVGTVLTAKY R
(2)	ANS.ANS	VHASLDKFLC	AVGTVLTAKY R
(3)	ANS.A.DO	VHASLDKFLC	AVGTVLTAKY R
(4)	BR.CAN	VHASLDKFLC	AVGTVLTAKY R
(5)	CYGN.0	VHASLDKFLC	AVGAVLTAKY R
(6)	ANA.P.P	VHASLDKFMC	AVGAVLTAKY R
(7)	ANA.P.DO	VHASLDKFMC	AVGAVLTAKY R
(8)	C.MOSCH	VHASLDKFMC	AVGAVLTAKY R
(9)	ANS.SEM	VHASMDKFLC	AVATVLTAKY R
(10)	STR.CAM	VHASLDKFLC	AVSAVLTAKY R
(11)	RHEA.AM	VHASLDKFLC	AVGAVLTAKY R
(12)	PHAS.COL	VHASLDKFLC	AVGTVLTAKY R
(13)	GALLUS	VHASLDKFLC	AVGTVLTAKY R
(14)	AQU.CH	VHASLDKFLC	AVGNVLTAKY R

mention that we are in Germany and Switzerland working on basic types of or within the Equidae, the Fringillidae, the Phasianidae, the Helicidae, the Hominidae and the Fagaceae.

Is it possible to verify this concept? One way of testing the hypothesis consists of palaeontological research. This will be one of the next projects. It is predicted from the model presented in this paper that:

1. *From the palaeontological record no links between the Anatidae and other birds should be found.*

2. *The phylogeny of Anatidae cannot be traced exactly in the palaeontological record.*

3. *There may be connecting links between tribes of Anatidae.*

However, this work can only be done in close correlation with the interpretation of post-Flood sedimentation. Theoretically we would expect a rapid adaptive radiation after the Flood in accordance with known mechanisms of micro-evolution within small groups of individuals. It should be emphasized that this remains speculative. Here is a wide area for creationists to develop suitable models of population dynamics.

The second way of testing our hypothesis is to consider the amino-acid sequences of bird haemoglobins. It is striking that the α–haemoglobins differ much more in birds than the β–haemoglobins (Godovac-Zimmermann & Braunitzer 1984). One interpretation would be that the members of a basic type had a common amino-acid sequence for α–haemoglobin in the beginning and diverged subsequently. By calculating the most probable ancestral sequence it can be seen that, on the average, the Anatidae show three amino-acid replacements (Table 3, Fig. 8). On the other hand the β–haemoglobin seemingly was common for all non-passerine birds, indepen-

---

Figure 8 Amino-acid sequences of α–haemoglobins of non-passerine birds. The one-letter code is used. The bibliography is given in Scherer & Sontag (1986).

1 = *Anser indicus*, 2 = *Anser anser*, 3 = *A. a. dom.*, 4 = *Branta canadensis*, 5 = *Cygnus olor*, 6 = *Anas platyrhynchos*, 7 = *A.p. dom.*, 8 = *Cairina moschata*, 9 = *Anseranas semi-palmata*, 10 = *Struthio camelus*, 11 = *Rhea americana*, 12 = *Phasianus colchicus*, 13 = *Gallus gallus*, 14 = *Aquila chrysaetos.*

dently of the basic type. This may be due to distinct functional requirements which cannot be discussed here in detail (compare Oberthür *et. al.* 1980). By elucidating the ancestral sequences of β–haemoglobin one can see in the birds three amino-acid replacements on average. This may point to identical times of divergence for both haemoglobins. (Note that the domestic duck has three amino-acid differences compared to the wild type! (Godovac-Zimmermann & Braunitzer 1983.) Based on the data available today I would postulate a basic-type-specific α–haemoglobin and a non-passerine bird-specific β–haemoglobin. The phylogenetic relationship then is monophyletic for the *Anatidae* and polyphyletic for the birds. By comparing more sequences we may hope to verify taxonomic and 'phylogenetic' models reflecting the creationist point of view of life. This is under investigation in the study group *Wort and Wissen* (Scherer & Binder, (unpubl.)).

α –haemoglobins			β –haemoglobins					
Position	Amino-acid		Position	Amino-acid				
34	Ile	Ile	4	Ser	Thr	Thr	Thr	Ser
115	Ser	Ser	43	Ala	Ser	Ala	Ser	Ser
134	Thr	Ala	135	Glu	Glu	Glu	Asp	Glu
x̄	3.0	3.0	x̄	3.1	3.3	3.1	3.5	3.3
±σ	1.6	1.0	±σ	1.1	1.5	1.3	1.9	1.6

Table 3: Possible ancestral sequences of α– and β–haemoglobin of non-passerine birds. The position of the amino-acids and some possible amino-acids at this position are specified. x̄ = average value of the amino-acid differences of all bird haemoglobins compared with the alleged ancestral sequences with ±σ = standard deviation. Please note that within the α–haemoglobins only the Anatidae are compared, but within the β–haemoglobins are included all non-passerine birds investigated so far. Of course, a variety of other ancestral sequences could have been constructed with very high deviations from the recent sequences (compare Fig. 8).

Limited variability?

It was speculated above that the basic type defines the limits
of variability. Comparing different breeding experiments with
animals like dogs, ducks, horses and so on, it can be stated
very clearly that, considering both morphological and biochemical peculiarities, the limits of the basic type have *never*
been exceeded. Unfortunately, we do not know the laws
determining variability in these cases, because nearly nothing
is known about the way biological patterns are being formed
in animals (Edelman, 1984). Therefore it is not possible to
speculate on the limits of variability of animals in terms of
molecular biology. However, many more experiments have
been done with procaryotes, and in the following section I
would like to point out some limits of variability of procaryotic
life.

Basic functional states

It is the aim of this section to study the evolution of a
particular biological process. The following principles have
been formulated (Scherer 1983a) to aid in the presentation of
this topic.

1. To investigate the change of functional biological
complexes is to investigate the change of genes and thence of
proteins. These changes must be based on principles which
can be described either experimentally or theoretically. There
is wide agreement in the scientific world that the most
important mechanisms leading to a quantitative increase in
genes is gene duplication, and the most common source of
qualitative gene changes is point mutation (e.g., Ohno 1970,
Koch 1972, Schilz 1981).

2. Each intermediate level between two functional states in
evolution must have some advantage compared to the former
state and thus it may be considered a stable intermediate
functional state.

3. The basic aims of evolutionary molecular biology are; (i)
to search for the minimal distance between two functional
states, denoted as a 'pair of basic functional states' between
which no stable intermediate state is possible; (ii) to find the

number of gene duplications and point mutations connecting a pair of basic functional states; and (iii) to calculate the probability that a given change from one basic state to another occurs by chance.

4. The only way to deal with these questions is to consider real examples, which is often impossible because it requires more detailed information concerning the molecular architecture of biological systems than is currently available.

I have used the example of the evolution of cyclic photosynthetic electron transport to demonstrate that the currently known principles of evolution are not suitable to explain the origin of completely new basic functional states (Scherer 1983a, 1983b, 1984). From this work one example is

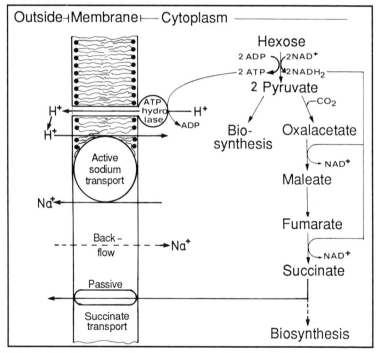

Figure 9 Fermentative energy metabolism of a hypothetical bacterium, similar to *Clostridium*. By using up the energy-rich components of the 'prebiotic soup', a selection pressure towards an indirect alkalization of the cytoplasm is thought to have originated. (Reprinted from Scherer 1983b).

presented below. For further details the reader is referred to the literature cited.

It is supposed that there was a reducing atmosphere on the early earth while the primitive oceans contained organic substances which were catabolized through fermentation (Fig. 9). Succinate as an end product of fermentation may have left the cell, depending on its concentration gradient, while the ATP produced is partially utilized as a proton pumping ATPase. It has been proposed by Broda & Peschek (1979)

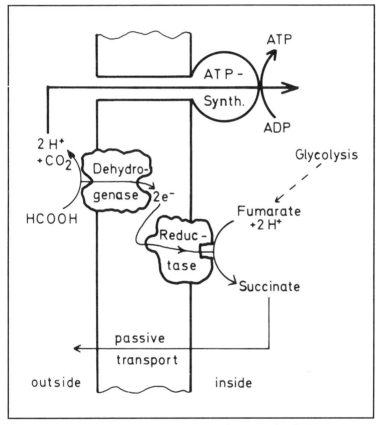

Figure 10 Cytoplasmic membrane of a hypothetical procaryote conserving energy by an indirect alkalization of the cytoplasm, which could have been the first new basic functional state following fermentative metabolism. (Reprinted from Scherer, 1984.)

that the next state could have been an indirect alkalization of the cytoplasm (Fig. 10). The soluble fumarate reductase becomes membrane-bound and formate dehydrogenase is formed *de novo*. The consequence would be that oxidation of extra-cellular fumarate creates a proton gradient without transmembrane proton translocation. Thus the cytoplasm becomes alkaline. If the pre-existing transport of ATPases becomes reversible, the proton gradient could be used for ATP synthesis. Considering the preconditions necessary for this step, some minimal requirements can be listed for which the estimated number of mutations is shown in Table 4.

	New function	point mutations
Gene 1	ATP hydrolase becomes reversible:	1
Gene 2	Soluble fumarate reductase becomes membrane bound, fumarate reductase:	3
	changes its specificity, binding formate dehydrogenase:	3
Gene 3	Gene duplication, the duplicate gene coding for the new formate dehydrogenase:	1
	Formation of a first catalytical site, cleaving formate:	3
	Formation of a second catalytical site, reducing fumarate dehydrogenase:	3

Table 4: Numbers of point mutations estimated to be necessary for creating a new basic functional state. (Although regulatory processes are absolutely necessary, these are not considered here!) Reprinted from Scherer, 1984.

The probability for the emergence of this new basic functional state, by means of evolutionary processes during a time interval of 10^9 years, has been estimated to be 10^{-100} to 10^{-16} depending on the mutation rate assumed (Scherer 1983a, 1983b). A similar result is found using the mechanisms of the neutral theory of evolution as suggested by Kimura (1982, Scherer 1984). However, it should be noted carefully that these estimations are based on the knowledge currently available — further experimental results may necessitate a re-examination.

Let us return to the basic type of the Anatidae. Due to our lack of knowledge, the above-mentioned arguments can only be presented for procaryotes. Nevertheless, if the emergence of a completely new basic functional state (differing from its precursor by only two enzymes) seems to be highly improbable within procaryotes, at least the same should be true for higher organisms such as the Anatidae. Based on this premise one may formulate the following hypothesis: *basic types are separated because basic functional states cannot be carried over into one another by means of evolutionary processes.*

This hypothesis involves a prediction: further molecular-biological research should uncover and describe these basic functional states. Then it can be estimated by experimental and theoretical work whether the separation of these states can or cannot be overcome by evolutionary processes. This research is an important aim for the future of both evolutionist and creationist biology.

Outlook

It is my impression that creationists should perform much more research on the variability of living things. In fact, we are far more interested in fast micro-evolutionary processes than evolutionists are and we may readily adopt the known principles of micro-evolution from the biological sciences. We should keep in mind that there may be principles of variability unknown so far, especially concerning the mutation of regulatory gene complexes. Perhaps the organisms surviving the Flood were more complex in their multiplicity of genetic equipment than are modern organisms. We know from evolutionary biology that speciation is coupled with the loss of genetic potential. The evolution of life within the boundaries of the basic type therefore may be an adaptation to different ecological niches; *not by evolutionary processes generating new information by chance but by controlled processes of variation based on sophisticated genetic programmes.* The biospecies may reflect the stable end-products of the diversification process (involving mutation, selection, neutral evolution, genetic drift, polymorphism, isolation and migration as well as other unknown processes) following creation and Flood. The 'biospecies' concept is not superfluous in a creationist biology; it should simply be supplemented by the 'basic type' concept.

Biologists know many examples of 'explosive variation' without any hint of specific selection pressure, and this seems to be a consequence of refined 'variation programmes' in the genome. It should be a challenge to creationist biologists to explore and decode these mechanisms.

Let us keep in mind that it is easy to set up great unifying hypotheses. The difficulties will arise in supporting these hypotheses with detailed studies in specialized fields, representing thorough and solid work. This work (who knows?) may significantly weaken our most cherished hypotheses. Perhaps the concept of basic types will eventually prove not to be of value in biology. Be that as it may, creationists should do such work. Otherwise they will contribute nothing of use to biology.

Bibliography

Andrews E.H., (1984) reply to *Creationism in confusion,* Nature (Lond)312, 396

Baba M.L., Darga D.L., Goodman M., Czelusniak J., (1981), *Evolution of cytochrome c investigated by the maximum parsimony method,* J.Mol.Evol. 17,197-213.

Bailey C.J., Geoffroy P., Mills K.H.G. (1976), *An examination of the distribution of hen- and goose-type lysozymes in Anseriformes.* Comp. Biochem. Physiol. 55B,429-433.

Broda E., Peschek G.A. (1979), *Did respiration or photosynthesis come first?* J. Theor. Biol. 81, 201-212.

Edelman G.M. (1984), *Cell adhesion molecules: A molecular basis for animal form.* Sci.American 250(4),80-91.

Fitch W.M., Margoliash E. (1967), *Construction of phylogenetic trees. A method based on mutation distances as estimated from cytochrome c sequences is of general applicability* Science 155,279-285.

Godovac-Zimmermann J., Braunitzer G. (1983), *The amino acid sequence of Northern Mallard (Anas platyrhyrnchos platyrhynchos) haemoglobin.* Hoppe Seyler's Z. Physiol. Chem. 364, 665-674.

Godovac-Zimmermann J., Braunitzer G. (1984), *The amino acid sequence of α- and β-chains from the major haemoglobin component of American Flamingo (Phoenicopterus ruber ruber).* Hoppe-Seyler's Z. Physiol. Chem. 365,437-443.

Gray A.P. (1958), *Bird hybrids — a checklist with bibliography.* L. Cunningham Ltd, Bucks.

Harrison C.J.O., ed., (1978), *Bird families of the world,* Elsevier-Phaidon, Oxford, pp.8-9.

Johnsgard P.A., (1978) *Ducks, swans and geese of the world,* University of Nebraska Press, Lincoln.

Kimura M., ed., (1982) *Molecular evolution, protein evolution and the neutral theory,* Jap.Sci.Soc.Press, Tokyo, Springer, Berlin-Heidelberg-New York.

Koch A.L. (1972), *Enzyme evolution: I. The importance of untranslatable intermediates,* Genetics 72,297-316.

Kuhn O. (1971), *Die vorzeitlichen Vögel,* Ziemsen-Verlag, Wittenberg.

Marsh F.L. (1947), *Evolution, Creation and Science,* Washington DC.

Marsh F.L. (1976), *Variation and fixity in nature,* Mountain View.

Mayr E. (1966) *Animal species and evolution,* Cambridge, Mass., Harvard University Press.

Mayr E. (1969), *Principles of systematic zoology,* New York, McGraw-Hill.

Milner A.R. (1981), *Flamingos, stilts and whales,* Nature (Lond) 289,347.

Oberthür W., Voelter W., Braunitzer G. (1980), *Die Sequenz der Hämoglobine von Streifengans (Anser indicus) und Strauß (Struthio camelus). Inositpentaphosphat als Modulator der Evolutionsgeschwindigkeit: Die überraschende Sequenz von alpha63(E12), Valin.* Hoppe-Seyler's Z. Physiol.Chem.161,969-975.

Ohno S. (1970), *Evolution by gene duplication,* Heidelberg, Berlin, New York, Springer.

Scherer S. (1983a), *Basic functional states in the evolution of light driven cyclic electron transport,* J.Theor. Biol. 104,289-299.

Scherer S., (1983b), *Photosynthese: Bedeutung und Entstehung — ein kritischer Überblick.,* Hänssler, Neuhausen-Stuttgart.

Scherer S. (1984), *Transmembrane electron transport and the neutral theory of evolution,* Origins of Life 14,725-731.

Scherer S., Binder H., Sontag C., (1985), *Occurence and amino acid sequences of cytochrome c and plastocyanin of algae and plants: Endocytobiotic implications.* Endocytobiol. Cell Res. 2,1-14.

Scherer S., Hilsberg T. (1982), *Hybridisierung und Verwandtschaftsgrade innerhalb der Anatidae — eine systematische und evolutionstheoretische Betrachtung.* J. Ornithol. 123,357-380.

Scherer S., Sontag C. (1983), *Phylogenetic and endosymbiotic implications of the amino acid sequences of 32 plant type ferredoxins.* In: *Endocytobiology II,* H.E.A. Schenk, W. Schwemmler (eds), Walter de Gruyter, Berlin-New York, pp. 863-870.

Scherer S., Sontag C. (1986), *Zur molekularen Taxonomie und Evolution der Anatidae.* Z. Zool. Syst. Evolutionsforsch. 24, 1-19.

Schulz G.E. (1981), *Protein-Differenzierung: Entwicklung neuartiger Proteine im Laufe der Evolution.* Angew. Chem. 93,143-151.

Schwabe C., Warr G.W. (1984), *A polyphyletic view of evolution: The genetic potential hypothesis.* Persp. Biol. Med. 27,465-485.

Siegler H.R. (1976), *Evolution or degeneration — which?,* Milwaukee, USA.

Siegler H.R. (1978), *A creationists' taxonomy,* Cre. Res. Soc. Quart. 15,36-38.

Steinhausen D., Langer K., (1977), *Clusteranalyse.* Walter de Gruyter, Berlin-New York.

Wackernagl H. (1972), *Brandente Tadorna tadorna x Eiderente Somateria mollissima, ein neuer Bastard bei den Entenvögeln.* Orn. Beob. 69,253-254.

Wolters H.E. (1975-1982), *Die Vogelarten der Erde,* Parey, Hamburg.

Woolfenden G.E. (1961), *Postcranial osteology of the water fowl,* Bull. Florida State Mus. 6,1-129.

Acknowledgements:

The data referred to in this paper have been worked out with the help of T. Hilsberg, Erlangen and C. Sontag, Konstanz. I would like to thank R. Wiskin, Oberlunkhofen, for improving the English text and my wife for stimulating discussion and for her patient help in preparing the manuscript.

10.

Genes — created but evolving

Chris Darnborough

Summary

Genetic mechanisms causing evolutionary change are described, and shown to be a reasonable basis for a limited evolutionary view of origins. The implications of the *de novo* creation of genes and genomes are discussed and the effects of evolutionary processes on such created entities are considered. It is concluded that the evolution of originally created genes is a good model for the origin of modern genomes and observed genetic phenomena.

Introduction

To the convinced anti-evolutionist the ideas put forward in this paper may appear unconventional and even heretical. The author is a biblical creationist who is also a molecular biologist, and constantly sees vast amounts of biological data being interpreted within an evolutionary framework. Such interpretations, although usually superfluous, are not always misleading or erroneous. Evolution at the level of genes and molecules, as process, is a reality which can be studied experimentally and which can bring about major genetic change in gene pools and natural populations. Such a view does not imply any agreement with evolutionism, either as a

model for organic origins or as a philosophy, nor does it lead
to a theistic evolutionary position.

In the beginning, when God created living things, he
necessarily created genes, since organic life and all its
characteristics are entirely determined by, and dependent
upon, the genes that encode it. It is true also that all life is
sustained by God, but that belief does not affect the way in
which we as scientists carry out experiments and interpret
them so long as we examine *process*, though it may affect the
ethics of our science. Thus the Bible-believing Christian has
no grounds on which to reject the validity of scientific methods
in studying evolutionary processes. To accept the extrapo-
lation of that process back to Genesis 1:1, however, is to deny
the Word of God, which tells us that the creation process was
different.

The opening chapters of Genesis do not tell us anything
about process. Thus we are unable, for instance, to make
scientific statements about the duration of the six creation
days, but we are able to deduce that God planned, designed
and created, *ex nihilo*, a universe that was 'very good'.
Combined with what we know about the nature of God, we
may then work out the essential characteristics of the living
world as newly created, at the moment when Adam first
stood, as a mature but newly formed being, in the garden
prepared for him. What had happened up to that moment we
may understand only from what God has revealed to us, by
faith (Heb. 11:3) and not in scientific terms. *Since* that
moment, the universe has been subject to physical laws of
which we may eventually have complete understanding.

From the moment of his creation Adam, and all nature with
him, has been evolving in some sense. Creation was a finished
act of God, but evolution is a continuing process of natural
law.

This paper seeks to discuss the effects of evolutionary
processes on a created living world, at the level of genes and
genetics. The scientific issues dealt with are necessarily highly
technical and are given in the text in somewhat simplified
form. Selected topics are amplified, with examples and
references, in the footnotes.[1]

Starting points

The Word of God is the only valid justification for a creationist view of origins. The impossibility of a chemical origin of life is a convincing basis for rejecting the evolutionary model of origins, but we must beware of assuming that rejection of chemical evolution necessarily leads to a creationist position. However, for the evolutionist, chemical evolution is an inescapable necessity, despite its lack of any experimental or theoretical basis. We do not need to enter into details here.[2] The problem, apart from the chemistry itself which does not work, is really a genetic one. Figure 1 expresses simply that a living cell is a bounded, self-replicating system

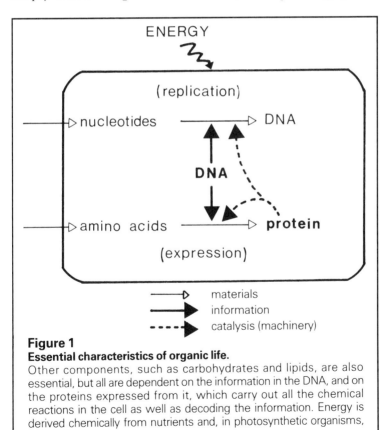

Figure 1
Essential characteristics of organic life.
Other components, such as carbohydrates and lipids, are also essential, but all are dependent on the information in the DNA, and on the proteins expressed from it, which carry out all the chemical reactions in the cell as well as decoding the information. Energy is derived chemically from nutrients and, in photosynthetic organisms, from light.

containing structures and information, in which the information (DNA sequences) is expressed by means of structures (protein molecules). These are themselves *products* of the expression of that information, as well as the means of expression. DNA, outside the context of the cellular machinery which decodes it, is an inert chemical. Information implies context and the context for genetic information is a consistent genetic code and appropriate transcription and translation mechanisms.

No credible model exists to explain the origin of such a system by naturalistic mechanisms. Only intelligent design (creation) is able to generate a living system.

Organic evolution?

If we allow the assumption that a primordial living cell did somehow emerge from the rather dilute primaeval soup, is it possible to progress further? The question first needs to be restated in genetic terms. Is it possible, by random processes, to achieve an increase, sustained over evolutionary time, in the informational complexity of a genome or population genepool? This is not to say that, for instance, man is more highly evolved than amoeba, but simply to recognize the fact that man is, by several orders of magnitude, genetically more complex than amoeba. Evolution as a theory of origins requires that the total informational complexity of individual genomes and of the entire biosphere has increased steadily through evolutionary time and presumably continues to increase. 'Information' here means a sequence of bases in DNA which, in the context of the cellular translation machinery, confers some selectable phenotype on the cell or organism.

The answer to the question is not a decisive 'Yes', but neither can it be a simple 'No'. Of the few perennially quoted examples which appear to support the evolutionary view, only the case of the peppered moth is readily explained away by natural selection rather than by the appearance of novel genetic information. It would be foolish to assert that genes for antibiotic resistance carried on bacterial plasmids were specially created; in bacteria it is certain that selectable phenotypes can arise by random modification of existing genes.[3]

At this level the evolutionist's position is a reasonable one, and it is likely that well-understood genetic mechanisms are capable of producing much more evolutionary change than most creationists are prepared to consider possible. Nevertheless, the limits of evolutionary change must remain a matter of speculation and argument. It is most unlikely that genetic mechanisms can account for transitions such as that from reptiles to birds, but it is likely that evolution occurs beyond the bounds of what is commonly called micro-evolution. The type of experiment required to demonstrate such processes is somewhat time-consuming.[4]

How evolution works[5]

Recent research in molecular genetics has revealed that the genome (DNA complement) of an organism is not so fixed as was once believed by even neo-Darwinists, who once relied on random mutation events as the major source of selectable genetic variation. It is now apparent that cells contain many normal mechanisms responsible for modifying, rearranging and translocating genes as aspects of essential cellular functions. DNA may also be transferred from one organism to another, and every mammalian genome contains much DNA integrated into the chromosomes which is of viral origin but related to cellular genes.

Mutation and natural selection — micro-evolution?
The vast majority of point mutations, small deletions and insertions are either neutral, deleterious or lethal. While it is possible that mutations at this level may confer selective advantage, and that point mutations in regulatory genes may have major developmental effects,[25] the generation of new genetic information requires more dramatic changes. The results of most experiments in which populations are mutagenized and then selected for specific mutant phenotypes over many generations demonstrate that there are limits to the extent of change that is possible. In general, selective pressures tend to be normalizing. In other words, even under

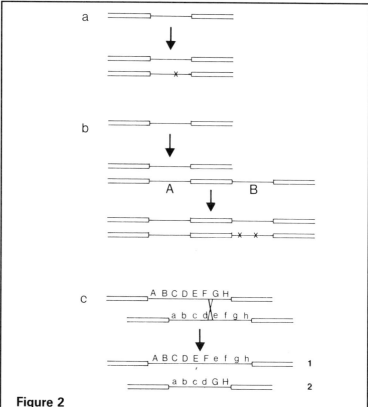

Figure 2
Some mechanisms for genetic change.
In each diagram a single line represents a gene or group of genes, while boxed sections are flanking regions of DNA. x represents a point mutation.
a) *Point mutation.* A single base change, a small deletion or insertion in one daughter chromosome during replication.
b) *Gene duplication.* A single gene is copied twice during replication, giving progeny genes A & B which initially are identical. One copy (A) must be conserved unchanged, or gene function will be lost or impaired, but (B) is not constrained by selection and is free to evolve.
c) *Unequal crossing-over in recombination.* In meiosis the maternal and paternal genes of homologous chromosomes are assorted by recombination, each daughter chromosome normally retaining a full complement of genes. Here recombination has resulted in one expanded chromsome (1) with additional genes, and one contracted (2) with consequent loss of genetic information. 2 will probably be a lethal mutation, while 1 has effectively duplicated a region of DNA, and may evolve as in b.

intensive selection, populations tend to retain or revert to the original phenotype. Such small, random mutations are apparently unable to generate new genetic information in experimental terms.[6]

Gene duplication — how to make more genes
It is possible during DNA replication for a single gene to be copied twice; indeed, for some genes this is a normal step in their expression.[7] Unequal crossing-over in meiosis is a further mechanism which may give rise to gene duplication (see below). As illustrated in Figure 2b, if both copies of the gene are retained, while one must remain functional and be conserved, the other may be mutated and become non-functional without reducing the fitness of the organism. As the mutated gene 'drifts' it may eventually acquire a new function with selective advantage to the organism and be fixed in the population, thus adding to the genome's informational complexity. All genomes of higher organisms contain families of genes that are structurally related in such a way as to suggest that they arose by this mechanism.[8] Pseudogenes may also arise in this way, being non-functional genes which are clearly related to a functional gene or gene family in sequence and organization, but which cannot be expressed. Pseudogenes may be seen as a source of genetic variation with considerable evolutionary potential.[9]

Examples of families of related genes are common, and include the genes of important proteins, such as globins (Fig. 3), immunoglobulins (Fig. 4) and actins, as well as those for the RNA molecules involved in the translation machinery. Immunoglobulin (antibody) genes are particularly important in evolutionary terms, because it is maintained that all antibody genes, and indeed the genes for many components of the immune system, are derived from a single ancestral immune response gene by duplications and mutation. The arguments in favour of this interpretation are very compelling, because it is clear that duplication and mutation of any existing immunoglobulin gene would be potentially advantageous because this would increase the repertoire of the immune system. Indeed in normal lymphocytes, immunoglobulin genes are first rearranged and then mutated by specific enzymes which exist to increase diversity and thus to enhance

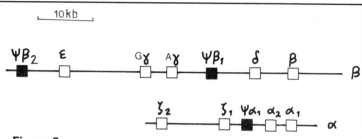

Figure 3
Organization of the two families of globin genes.
Every haemoglobin molecule contains four protein chains of the type $\alpha_2\beta_2$, but the α-like and β-like genes differ at different stages of development, e.g. $\alpha_2\gamma_2$ in the foetus switches to $\alpha_2\beta_2$ in the adult. All the globin genes are similar (homologous) in sequence. Open boxes represent functional genes; closed boxes are pseudogenes, which are closely similar to the functional genes, but are defective in their regulatory sequences and mutated in coding sequences and are not expressed. The scale shows 10 kb (10,000 base pairs) of DNA.

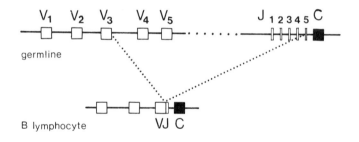

Figure 4
Immunoglobulin genes rearrangement (light chains).
During the differentiation of B lymphocytes (antibody producing cells), functional immunoglobulin genes are formed by joining one of a large number of V (variable) region genes to one of a small number of J (joining) region genes which is next to a C (constant) region gene. The DNA between V and J is deleted. Subsequently the VJ region of the rearranged gene is subject to a high rate of point mutation to further increase the variability of the antibody proteins. These processes bring about the clonal expression (a single immunoglobulin gene within a single cell lineage) of antibody genes, and allow the vast antibody diversity and fine tuning of the immune response which is essential for an efficient immune system. Many V genes, perhaps 50%, are pseudogenes.

the efficiency of the immune system.[10] It is probable that immunoglobulin gene families, which contain many pseudo-genes, do evolve by this mechanism, but to explain the origin of the entire immune system in this way is in clear conflict with the creation of a complete organism with a functional immune system.

Recombination — mixing up genes.
The mechanisms that exist in germ cells to maintain genetic variation by assorting the gene complements of homologous chromosomes in meiosis also present opportunities for generating new genetic information. Aberrant processes such as unequal crossing-over and gene conversion (which could also function as a sort of proof-reading system for maintaining uniformity within certain gene families) may join together segments of different genes to yield a chimeric gene, or give rise to gene duplication (Fig. 2c). The evolutionary potential of such events is as described above, and examples of chimeric genes do exist.[11] Gene conversion has been invoked as an explanation of the coincidental evolution of gene families in which many identical copies are conserved over evolutionary time — a mechanism for resisting change by inducing change!

Specific recombination mechanisms exist in some somatic cells also as a means of generating diversity, including the rearrangement of antibody genes in lymphocytes[10] and the variation in surface antigens of trypanosomes[10(b)], which is a mechanism for evading the immune response. Figure 4 illustrates the rearrangement of immunoglobulin genes.

Mobile genetic elements — moving genes
Bacteria in particular, and higher organisms as well, contain many small pieces of DNA (insertion sequences, transposons) which may be replicated independently (plasmids, episomes, viruses) and which are able to integrate into and be excised from the chromosome, either at specific sites or at random. Figure 5 illustrates some bacterial mobile elements. Such DNA elements often pick up fragments of chromosomal DNA and can then transfer them to different positions in the genome, to a different cell, and perhaps to a different species. Mobile elements in higher organisms mediate a number of normal cellular processes, including the quasi-inheritable

serotype switching in trypanosomes already mentioned. Other examples are the mobile elements which control a wide variety of genetic *loci* in maize, mating type switches in yeast, and *copia* elements in *Drosophila*.[12] As well as controlling essential genetic processes, mobile elements in the genome have been implicated as causes of cancer and other diseases, and sequences transposed by mobile elements are often subject to high rates of mutation. In evolutionary terms the ability to transfer genetic material from one organism to another is clearly a powerful mechanism for acquiring new genetic information.[13]

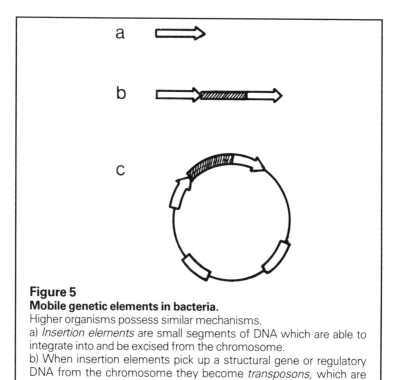

Figure 5
Mobile genetic elements in bacteria.
Higher organisms possess similar mechanisms.
a) *Insertion elements* are small segments of DNA which are able to integrate into and be excised from the chromosome.
b) When insertion elements pick up a structural gene or regulatory DNA from the chromosome they become *transposons,* which are able to move segments of DNA around the genome.
c) If a transposon acquires a DNA segment which is able to function as an initiator of replication, it may become a *plasmid,* an independently replicating genetic element which grows to high copy numbers within the cell, and may be transferred to other cells, maybe even to different species of bacteria. Many antibiotic resistance genes are carried on plasmids.

Mobile genetic elements also have practical value, and are used in the technology of genetic engineering to investigate the mechanisms of gene expression and to introduce genes for many medically and commercially valuable protein products into bacteria.[14]

Junk DNA and selfish DNA — evolution's scrapyard?

Bacteria, in general, compete for the resources available in the environment primarily by means of growth rate, and thus it is important to minimize the size of the genome so that DNA replication time is minimized. This probably explains why in simple single-cell organisms every base in the DNA has some essential function. In higher organisms, where selection pressures on the genome are more subtle, a large proportion of the DNA has no known function either in coding for, or in controlling the expression of, cellular proteins. Such DNA sequences, which must arise by means of the mechanisms discussed above, are not constrained by any known selective pressures, and are free to evolve independently of the rest of the genome. However, just as a pile of scrapped motor cars contains bits and pieces which are of value to somebody, in evolutionary terms this unwanted collection of DNA sequences is a potential source of new gene functions. This selective potential may be the only selection pressure that maintains such sequences in the genome.[15]

Evolution has a mechanism

This brief survey of normal and aberrant, but experimentally verifiable, mechanisms for genetic change provides clear evidence that evolutionary changes leading to increasing genome complexity can and do occur. It is true that such an increase in complexity has not been demonstrated experimentally, but in many cases it is clearly indicated by genetic data, and it is likely that as genetic engineering techniques become more powerful, direct correlations between DNA sequence and novel gene function will be made.[16,17] Information Theory has also been used to argue against the possibility of novel genetic information arising by random processes, which in a closed system can never result in an increase in the amount of information. It is not clear whether Information Theory is applicable to biological systems in general, but it can certainly be argued that genetic processes are not truly random in the sense required, and that the existence of mobile genetic elements invalidates any concept of an organism as a closed system in informational terms.[18]

Evolution has a mechanism. To deny that assertion is to reject a vast amount of valid experimental data.

Homology — not a process
Evolutionism views all homology — similarities between fossil or living organisms at the morphological or molecular level — as a consequence of common ancestry and evolutionary trees are constructed on the basis of such relationships. However, as recent debates over the applications of cladistics have demonstrated,[19] homology tells us about evolution only if evolution is assumed. More specifically, it can assist our understanding of evolutionary processes only if an ancestral relationship exists. Nevertheless it is true that evolutionary processes will generate homology at certain levels.

The subject of homology deserves much fuller discussion than is possible in this paper, as it serves as a point of contact between the creation and evolution models. This is because the creationist views homology as a natural consequence of design, and therefore expects to see similarities within and between organisms at every level of structure and complexity. At the same time certain homologies, even if only at the trivial level of those between different breeds of dog, for instance, must be acknowledged to be evolutionary in origin.[20]

Both purposeful design and random change, therefore, must be seen as having contributed to the pattern of both diversity and uniformity in the living world.

A 'good' creation — the perfect genome?

We must now turn to the biblical assertion that all living things were created mature and complete and perfect by an intelligent, logical and all-powerful Designer and Maker. What would be the genetic characteristics of such a creation, and what would be the effects upon it of the evolutionary processes we have discussed?

Adam, in common with all other living things, was brought forth from the dust of the earth. It is pointless to speculate over the processes used to achieve this, as evolutionists would have us do, because we are not able to understand the mind and the power of God in creation. We may infer that at the end of the creation period, on the evening of the sixth day, there existed a biosphere which was complete and mature, in which every organism was specifically designed and individually created, made to be perfectly adapted to its environment (or vice versa!). While it is possible to speculate about the sizes and characteristics of animal populations, we are told clearly that there was one man and one woman. Because they had not yet sinned the creation was 'very good' and not yet subject to the 'bondage to decay' described by Paul in Romans 8. It was without blemish.

Every structural detail of Adam's physical body, and the genetic information encoding that structure and the development and structure of his descendants, was perfectly adapted to the environment. Within that environment (Eden) no 'improvement' — new adaptations or increased fitness — was either possible or desirable; only deterioration could occur. We do not know whether Adam was created to live for ever as a physical being — whether indeed he was growing old — but even after the Fall he and many generations to follow lived for a very long time by modern standards. Neither do we know how complex his genome was. It may have been more or less complex than the modern human genome and it may have contained selfish DNA, pseudogenes and mobile genetic elements as long as these components could have no deleterious effects. In other words, Adam's genome may have been created with the genetic potential for evolution, but without having itself evolved; we do not know.

We may also speculate about Eve's genome. This is important because in sexually reproducing organisms the level of genetic variation is vastly increased by the combining of two individual genomes from egg and sperm. It is possible to take the view that Eve was 'cloned' from Adam's rib, by analogy with experiments performed on frogs, but the answer cannot be so simple because she must have differed genetically from Adam if only in her X/Y chromosome complement. We might also predict a significant level of allelic variation between their two genomes, which would eventually generate by recombination, without any need for mutation, a vast amount of diversity within the human population. This would be true of all species and it is consistent with our understanding of God, who would surely rejoice in the diversity of his creation.

Fall . . .

The origin of evolution, in its modern sense of a process of random change, is concisely summarized in Romans 8:20: 'The creation was subjected to futility' (RSV). It had not always been subject to futility, but 'lost its purpose' (Rom. 8:20, Good News Bible). The implication of this statement for biology and genetics is that for a period of time the creation was not at the mercy of random processes leading to corruption and death, but that such processes were restrained, either inherently by the genetic make-up of life, or externally by the power of God. The fall of Adam from grace brought a curse on man, on the ground and on all creation (Gen. 3:14-19). Through his Word, the Creator subjected his good creation to futility — to evolution. Our use of the word here does not include all that is implied by evolutionism, but does not exclude anything of evolutionary process.

. . . and decline

It has already been argued that the only possible effects of genetic change on a good creation would be deleterious. Thus any mutation events in the genome would tend to impair gene function or to subvert normal genetic processes to modify genome organization and impair gene regulation. The major source of the classical ingredients of neo-Darwinian evolution, mutation and natural selection, is the environment. Normal cellular mechanisms in some cases induce mutation, but these operate only in somatic cells. The germline (hereditary DNA) is subjected to copying errors in DNA replication, which at a frequency of 1 in 10^{10} to 1 in 10^9 contribute a negligible amount of genetic diversity. However, in addition aberrant recombination events in germ cells during meiosis may give rise to gene duplication, as we have seen, but subsequent mutation is required in order to generate new gene functions. All cells, germline and somatic, are subject to environmental mutagenesis, which is mediated by chemical mutagens and by a vast spectrum of ionizing radiations, all of which cause random genetic damage.

The Garden of Eden was a special, protected environment and we are not told anything about the state of the world outside Eden prior to the Fall. However, when Adam and Eve were cast out of Eden they were thrust into a harsh environment filled with spiritual and material pollution, violent death and competition. Their new habitat provided selection pressure able to accept or reject the mutations which it also induced. Populations increased rapidly and evolution was well under way. In the initial small populations many deleterious mutations must have become fixed, but if the fitness of the human genome is judged in terms of fertility and life span, little deterioration in the human gene pool was apparent before the time of Noah.

The environmental impact of the Flood (Gen. 6-9) must have been greater, in quantitative terms, than that of the Fall. All surviving terrestrial species passed through a population bottle-neck which would have a major effect on gene pools which already were accumulating deleterious mutations. The following factors may be considered as contributing to the first major 'punctuation' of the relative equilibrium of antediluvian life.

1. Inbreeding within small populations results in the fixation of many deleterious mutations and in the human population a consequent increase in genetic load (discussed more fully later).[21]

2. The extreme environments generated by the Flood, and radiative movements of animals into them, produced correspondingly extreme selection pressures and maintained small breeding populations for a long period. Many speciation events would result.

3. The 'Canopy Theory' proposes that the waters of the firmament which contributed to the flood waters had previously formed a protective canopy shielding the earth's surface from ionizing radiation. The removal of this canopy

would increase the rate of radiation-induced mutation and fuel the evolutionary processes.[22]

The conditions resulting from the Flood are therefore those which favour speciation in the conventional evolutionary model — genetic drift in small geographically isolated populations leading to reproductive isolation and hence speciation. It can be argued that the pattern of diversity arising within created kinds in a relatively short time under such conditions is comparable to the diversity resulting from evolution from a common ancestor over the vast time scales required by neo-Darwinian evolution. The time-scale requirements for the two models differ because of the different initial conditions and the direction of evolutionary change required.

Evolution — which way?

While neo-Darwinian evolution proceeds from a single ancestral species in the direction of increasing genome complexity, creation begins with an (unknown) number of complex genomes, each of which evolves independently (although in competition). The direction of change is indeterminate, as no increase in genome informational content is required, but diversity within kinds must increase. Genetic barriers prevent interbreeding between kinds, but convergent evolution may blur distinctions between kinds. Figure 6 illustrates the way in which the two models affect our interpretation of evolutionary trees and shows how either model adequately explains the patterns of diversity found within the fossil record and among modern species.

It must now be apparent that the argument with evolutionists is not really about process, but about ancestry — primordial blob versus mature kinds — and about the direction of evolutionary change — 'up' or 'down' or sideways. Much of the debate will continue to centre on the fossil record, which is admittedly difficult to reconcile with the creation model, but at the level of evolutionary processes, the argument is strongly in favour of creation. It is time to look at the evolution of created genomes.

The evolved gene — evidence of design?

Before looking for evidence of change it is relevant to ask whether evidences of the perfection of originally created genes are discernible in modern evolved genomes. At a detailed level it is impossible to answer this question, but the old 'argument from design' is still valid at the molecular level. In the light of our earlier consideration of the feasibility of a chemical origin of life, the most powerful argument for the creation of genes is that genes exist, and that even the simplest organisms utilize the sophisticated gene expression mechanisms found in higher organisms. There remains no trace of any putative primitive gene expression system or of any biological information system simpler than that which is ubiquitous in modern organisms. The design argument also includes the question of homology, discussed earlier.

A full understanding of molecular homology requires knowledge of the constraints on protein structure, and thus amino-acid sequence, which determine whether a protein

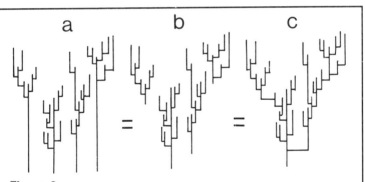

Figure 6
Hypothetical evolutionary trees.
The vertical axis represents time (scales may differ), the horizontal axis shows morphology, DNA sequence, or other aspects of variation. *The data* (tree b) are incomplete, showing many trees with gaps between them. The gaps may be dealt with 1) by adding vertical lines (tree a) - or no lines (tree b) - giving many trees each rooted in a *created kind*, as revealed by Scripture, or 2) by adding horizontal lines (tree c) representing hypothetical transitional forms, rooting all the trees in a single *common ancestor* as required by the theory of evolution. In each model the mechanisms for genetic change are identical.[26]

molecule will perform a given function. These constraints vary, since certain functions may be performed by a wide range of protein structures, while others show very little variation over a wide range of species. Thus the amino-acid sequence (and therefore the gene coding region) of histone Hl is very highly conserved across all eukaryotic species, indicating that only a very narrow range of structures is able to carry out its very specific function in binding to DNA in the chromatin. This in itself tells us nothing about the origin of the gene, or of species. On the other hand, amino-acid sequences of cytochrome c have been found to show much greater variation, and the structure is clearly less constrained. The evolutionary trees constructed from such molecular data may be treated in the way described in Figure 6. However, there are fundamental differences in interpretation between the two models. In the evolution model, all similarities are a consequence of common ancestry; differences are a consequence of divergent evolution; and the main determinant of protein structure, namely functional constraints, is bypassed. In the creation model, similarities result from functional constraints in design, while differences may also be introduced by design to optimize protein function in particular cellular environments. Further differences will then arise from evolutionary divergence, the extent of which will be limited by functional constraints (as it is in the evolution model also).

Thus although we may determine which features of protein structures are highly conserved, and therefore functionally indispensable, it is impossible to predict optimal structures encoded by the hypothetical 'perfect' genome. Nevertheless the evolution of created genes adequately explains observed patterns of molecular homology and is a more realistic framework for interpreting homology on a functional basis.[20]

The evolved genome — gene disorganization
The changes in gene structure discussed so far have been limited to point mutations in structural genes and the effects of natural selection on modified protein functions. Now we consider the effects of other evolutionary processes, described earlier, on the organization and expression of created genomes. These effects may include the generation of new genetic information in the ways already described, but are more likely

to lead to deleterious effects, either on protein coding sequences or on gene organization and the control of gene expression. In this section the emphasis will be on deleterious effects.

Pseudogenes may arise by mutation of gene duplications, or from individual members of gene families which become non-functional by mutating without gene duplication. The loss of a member of a gene family would normally be highly disadvantageous, but such events might be tolerated, for example, in immunoglobulin gene families, which contain many pseudogenes.

Genes or gene fragments may be moved to new locations in the genome with or without duplication or mutation. One possible consequence of such changes is to bring genes under the control of different controlling elements, such as hormonal regulation, and although most such regulatory changes will be deleterious or lethal, some may have evolutionary potential. The best studied examples of changes in gene regulation leading to major phenotypic effects are a group of genes called oncogenes, so named because they are all implicated in causing cancer. Most oncogenes are in fact perfectly normal genes whose protein products are involved in the control of cell division and the cell cycle, and many of them are expressed in a cell cycle specific manner. It is when the control of cell division is disrupted by deregulating these genes that they become tumorigenic. This can happen in at least two ways, apart from simple mutation of their regulatory elements. In many lymphomas and leukemias an aberrant immunoglobulin gene rearrangement has brought an 'oncogene' under the control of immunoglobulin gene regulation. These events always also involve a chromosome translocation (see below). It is probable that very many such aberrant rearrangements take place during lymphocyte differentiation, but most of them are never detected because they are lethal to the cell. Only those immortalized as tumours can be observed.

Cancer may also be caused by tumour viruses, and these include retroviruses, many of which contain mutated copies of cellular oncogenes as well as other genes taken out of the genome by various mobile elements. Every mammalian genome appears to contain retrovirus sequences integrated into the genome at high frequency.[23] These, although normally latent, may be activated to become pathogenic or carcinogenic. Virus infection may, of course, have similar consequences. Most cancers involve somatic cell types, but similar mechanisms to these may be implicated in teratocarcinomas and in teratogenesis — developmental abnormalities in the embryo — and presumably also affect germline cells.

Chromosome translocations, in which sections of two different chromosomes become joined, would normally be lethal, but are occasionally preserved as tumours, as described above. Translocations can also be carried in the germline and cause a number of inherited defects, as does polyploidy — more than two copies of a chromosome resulting from defective chromosome segregation at mitosis. Again, events such as these are probably frequent but rarely survive.[24]

In summary, the effect of evolutionary change will be· to move from a highly ordered genome towards one which is less ordered and which, though it may contain additional and novel genetic information, also contains much additional functionless DNA. This is potentially a source of new genetic information but is also potentially deleterious. This is a fair description of a modern genome and of the general observed direction of change.

Genetic load — an evolutionary burden

A major genetic problem for the human species, and for many populations of domestic animals, is that they are not in general subject to natural selection as most animal populations are. Thus many deleterious mutations and genetic defects, which would normally be eliminated from a population by selective pressures, are retained and propagated. Ironically the problem is exacerbated by modern medicine, which as it seeks, rightly, to treat a wide range of genetically inherited diseases, also succeeds in increasing the incidence of those disorders and of the defective genes which cause them. For instance, since the discovery of insulin the incidence of childhood diabetes and the lifespan and fertility of diabetics have been increasing steadily, along with the frequency of those HLA genotypes which are known to predispose individuals to diabetes. This is particularly true in the Western world, but such paradoxes occur in less developed nations as a consequence of natural selection. The sickle-cell trait, a severely debilitating disease caused by a mutant globin gene, is very common in certain areas of Africa because the defective red blood cells which characterize the trait are resistant to the malaria parasite.[27]

Genetic load is perhaps the clearest indication of the direction in which evolution normally proceeds. Its effects can be measured over periods of years at present, but can be traced back in biblical history to the early chapters of Genesis. It can be argued that the decline in human lifespans following the Flood, from 950 years (Noah) to 175 years (Abraham — a good old age), is correlated with increasing genetic load resulting from (1) inbreeding and (2) rapid evolution of the human gene pool.[28] The somewhat simplistic reasoning assumes that death occurs when the residual genetic information in the organism is no longer sufficient to overcome the Second Law of Thermodynamics. From conception, the inherited genetic information in all the cells of the organism is being slowly degraded and this certainly contributes to the ageing process. If the fertilized egg begins its development with a significant mutational burden, ageing will be more rapid and death correspondingly sooner.

However, the genetic basis of ageing is unclear. Recent work on animal tissue culture cells has suggested the idea of 'programmed senescence', because it appears that certain animal cells (more accurately, cell lineages) are genetically programmed to die after a fixed number of cell divisions. It is not clear whether this property is true of the same cells in their normal environment *in vivo*, and it is possible also that senescence is related to genetic load, but there are instances in which cell death must be seen as a normal and essential differentiation event in particular cell lineages. [29] We may speculate as to whether programmed senescence is a consequence of evolution or a more specific aspect of the Curse. Whatever the genetic basis, the effect is summarized in Genesis 2:17 'Dying you shall die.'

Ambiguities

The argument in this paper has been in very general terms. It will be apparent that any attempt to study the origin of a particular gene leads to the conclusion that the evidence is consistent with either of the two models. In the view of the author the only soundly based exception to this is that of chemical origins. In any other detail the evidence of science is ambiguous, and we should be wary of the temptation to argue from science to Scripture. Our entire presentation of the creation model must begin with Scripture, or it will fail. Equally, scientific ignorance or unsoundness will not honour the Creator and will deviate from the truth.

References

1. The aim of this paper is to suggest ways in which demonstrable genetic mechanisms for evolutionary change are consistent with the creationist model of origins. The genetic processes discussed are highly technical and are given in simplified terms. Only minimal references to research articles and reviews will be given, and for ease of access most are from the journal *Nature*; more will be found in any standard text on molecular evolution, although it must be recognized that all such texts are committed to an evolutionistic view of genetics as the basis of interpretation *and* description of genetic processes. For a recent creationist view of mutation see Leslie, J.G., *Ex Nihilo*, vol.6 no.4 pp.38-45.

2. For a fuller treatment of chemical evolution, see Wilder-Smith, A.E., *The creation of life: a cybernetic approach to evolution*, Harold Shaw, Wheaton, Illinois, (1970); Peet, J.H.J., *Thinking again about the origin of life* (Biblical Creation Society, 1983); Gish, D., *Speculations and experiments on the origin of life* (Institute for Creation Research, 1975); Aw, S.E., *Chemical Evolution* (Master Books, 1982); Thaxton, C.B., Bradley, W.L. and Olsen, R.L., *The Mystery of Life's Origin* (Philosophical Library, N.Y., 1984).

3. Because of the small generation times of bacteria, mutation events occurring at a frequency of 1 in 10^8 cells or less can be detected. When phenotypes such as antibiotic resistance, or ability to use hydrocarbons as a carbon source, may be selected from populations originating from a single cell (which lacked the selected phenotype), with a genome size of 10^6-10^7 base pairs of DNA, it is not possible that previously existing genetic information is being selected. It therefore appeared by evolutionary processes.

4. It is, however, significant that no 'speciation' event has been documented after years of such experiments with bacteria (see above). Experiments with *Drosophila* involving mutagenesis and selection over many generations have demonstrated that most selection is normalizing, and populations tend to retain or to revert to the original phenotype.

5. For a good review, with further references, see Hunkapillar, T. *et al* (1982) 'The impact of modern genetics on evolutionary theory,' in *Perspectives on evolution,* ed. R. Milkman (Sinauer Associates) pp. 164-189.

6. It appears that in protein sequences regarded as evolving on accepted evolutionary pathways, the frequency of deletion events exceeds that of insertions (deJong, W.W. & Ryden, L. (1981) *Nature 290,* 157). The implication is that proteins become smaller as they evolve!

7. Chisholm, R. (1982) 'Gene amplification during development.' *Trends in Biochemical Sciences, 7,* 1-2.

8. The genes for ribosomal RNA and transfer RNA are further important examples of gene families, with problems for both the creation and evolution models. See Jeffreys, A.J. and Harris, S. (1982) Processes of gene duplication. *Nature* (News & Views) *296,* 9; Dover, G. & Coen, E. (1981) *Nature* (News & Views *290,* 731.

9. Li, W. *et al* (1981) Pseudogenes as a paradigm of neutral evolution. *Nature 292,* 237.
Pseudogenes of a different type can also arise by insertion of a cDNA copy of a messenger RNA into the genome.

10. For reviews of antibody gene organization and expression see
(a) Tonegawa, S. (1983) *Nature 302,* 575
(b) Robertson, M. (1982) *Nature* (News & Views) *297,* 184

11. For example, chimaeras of haemoglobins and of immunoglobulin isotypes exist in man and mouse. Whether such events have given rise to novel protein functions in evolution is a matter of speculation. The point is that the mechanism exists and such recombination events do occur and may be stably inherited.

12. For reviews, see Bishop, J.M. (1978) *Ann. Rev. Biochem. 47,* 35-38 (on retroviruses); Bukhari, A.I., Shapiro, J.A., Adhya, S. *DNA insertion elements, plasmids and episomes.* Cold Spring Harbor Laboratory, C.S.H. New York (1977); Naevers, P. & Saedler, H. (1977) *Nature 268,* 109-115.

13. Transposition of regulatory DNA sequences will also have major phenotypic effects. An entire set of genes may be brought under the control of a different regulator gene, or of a hormone. Events of this type are implicated in certain cancers and in other

diseases. The oncogenic bacterium, *A. tumefaciens*, is able to cause tumours in plants because it carries a large plasmid (T_i) which transfects and then transforms plant cells into tumour cells.

14. *E. coli* bacteria have been engineered to synthesize human insulin, growth hormone, interferon and other expensive products with medical or commercial value.

15. For a summary of ideas on selfish DNA see short articles by Orgel, Crick & Sapienza; Dover & Doolittle; Jain, in *Nature 288*, 645-648 (1980). Selfish genes have also been discussed in relation to sociology and politics. For an example see letter by Dawkins, *Nature 289*, 528 (1981).

16. In bacteria such correlations can already be demonstrated.

17. Interspecies and intraspecies homologies at the molecular level are often compellingly consistent with derivation from common ancestors by the mechanisms described. At this level, the evolution model is very consistent with the facts. However, see notes on homology below (note 20).

18. It is possible to build computer models of gene expression by viewing DNA as a machine code. Such models are inadequate, partly because the genome is a digital information system, whereas the expression machinery and the resulting phenotype are analogue systems. We simply do not know the rules, and it is certain also that biological information violates the rules of Information Theory.

19. Patterson, C. 'Cladistics and Classification', *New Scientist*, 29 April 1982, p.303.

20. The example given here (dog kind) is actually trivial, because it is small differences between breeds that are significant at the genetic level. However, molecular homology is a point of contact between creation and evolution because in the final (or present) product, the structure or genotype, whether designed or evolved (or both), is constrained by the function or phenotype to which it is now adapted. (This explains why evolutionists often find themselves describing evolutionary events in teleological terms — eg David Attenborough, *Life on Earth*, BBC TV.) Consequently it is not possible, in principle, to determine whether a particular feature of homology results from design or from evolutionary adaptation of an ancestral feature, without making an assumption. This problem applies less to DNA sequences, which are less constrained than protein sequence because of redundancy in the genetic code. A detailed analysis of codon usage, which varies in specific ways from organism to organism and from protein to protein, might allow the development of rules which could distinguish design and ancestry.

21. Inbreeding was later outlawed in the law of Moses, for sound genetic reasons.
22. The writer does not subscribe to many detailed aspects of flood geology, and is unconvinced by the arguments for the canopy theory. The implications for evolution are nevertheless worth considering.
23. About 0.1% (3×10^6 base pairs) of the mouse genome is derived from retrovirus sequences. Many such mobile elements probably parasitize the mammalian genome.
24. Many chromosome translocations, some with major developmental effects, have been characterized in *Drosophila*, which seems to tolerate such changes remarkably well, as many such mutants are viable in natural populations. In mammals most translocations are lethal or associated with major developmental or physiological defects.
25. There are instances in which a small mutation event in even a structural gene may have major developmental effects. The *unc*54 (*unc* for unco-ordinated) mutation in the nematode worm, *C. elegans*, is a behavioural mutant which results from incomplete development of the nervous system. The genetic lesion is a deletion of about 20 bp in a structural gene for a muscle protein, which alters the differentiation pathway of a cell lineage in the developing nervous system (Brenner, unpublished). The change is in the opposite direction to that required for 'upward' evolution (increasing complexity), and would need to be reversed (a highly improbable event) to generate a mobile worm from an immobile, but viable one. Nevertheless the amount of genetic change required to achieve such a major evolutionary step is small.
26. i. The form in which Figure 6 is drawn is not intended to imply a particular mode of evolution (gradualism or punctuation).
    ii. In both models there are uncertainties concerning time scales, the nature of created kinds, transitional forms, etc. Note, however, that in the creation model, the *extent* of change is constrained by the rate of change and by time since creation. In evolution the *time scale* is constrained by rate of change and by the total extent of evolution required. It is not my purpose to discuss the fossil record, which is crucial here, and which has its own problems for both creation and evolution.
    iii. The creation model (a) implies nothing about the 'direction' of evolution; (c) requires a progression from simple to complex forms.
27. Strangely, this phenomenon is oft quoted as an example of evolutionary progress. However, despite a marginal selective

advantage — individuals with sickle trait are less likely to die of malaria — it is clear that the inherent fitness of sickle genomes is lower than non-sickle. Sickle cell trait results from the heterozygous condition (one copy of the HbS gene). Homozygosity (both genes HbS) is severely debilitating or fatal. Moreover, there is no increase in genome complexity.

28. Dietary changes also followed the Flood (Genesis 9:3).

29. In the study of cell lineages in nematodes[25], it is found that some lineages progress by division of a cell into two different daughter cells, one of which differentiates further while the other *invariably* dies. This cell death, which follows cell division, must be determined genetically. It could be caused negatively, by a specific genetic defect induced at cell division, or positively, by inducing a gene for an intracellular toxin, for instance. Some fully differentiated cells (e.g. red blood cells) die because the DNA is degraded at a specific stage in their development.

—